Nutrition Program Guide
by Jenny Ridgwell

You can log into the Nutrition Program at www.nutritionprogram.co.uk.

This book provides a step by step guide to help you get started with using the Nutrition Program. Students can work their way through the tasks and compare results.

ISBN-978-1-901151-96-1
Published by Ridgwell Press PO Box 202 Lewes BN7 9GT

Nutrition Program Guide

Contents

How to use The Nutrition Program

The Program has 3 sections
- My Recipes
- My Diets
- My Meals

My Recipes
Choose My Recipes, then click Create a new recipe.
Enter the recipe name and portions – Scones, 8.
Add ingredients and put the ingredient in Find ingredient – for example, flour.
A list of flours is shown and you must click one to choose. Flour, white, self raising, wheat.
Enter an amount. Type the amount in grams – the program gives you some clues but use your recipe. Flour 200g.
You may want to look at the Nutritional information for an ingredient such as Sunflower seeds.
Click to Enter the amount and then View Nutrition info.
When the recipe is complete, Save it by clicking on the Save button.
The recipe is now in your list of My Recipes.

Cost of the recipe.
Click on the recipe. Click on Cost Analysis.There is a list showing
- Name of ingredients
- Amount used
- Cost for 100g
- Cost recipe
- Cost portion.
The chart gives total weight of the recipe, the total cost for 100g, recipe and portion.

Nutrition Information
In the Nutrition Info there are three sections:4 8 Show all.
- The 4 section shows energy, protein, carbohydrate and fat.
- You can see the ingredients of the recipe listed in order of weight. The first 3 show the % by weight that they are in the recipe.
- The 8 section shows energy, protein, carbohydrate, total sugars, fat, saturated fat, fibre, salt, sodium.
- The 8 section also shows details per 100g, per portion, GDA women, GDA men, GDA child, and the traffic light colours. It also shows the net weight and allergens.
- You can click the GDA chart and Ingredients chart as well as exporting the information to use in your work.
- The Show all section has all the nutrients that are found in the food product.Create the food label

Click the section for Food Label.
In Recipe info, type in Storage information, Made by and Shelf life. The Storage information is how to store the product after it is made. So Scones could be stored in a dry, cool place.
Made by can be the person or company that has made it – so Jenny's bakery.
The Shelf life is how long it will last and remain safe. Scones will last 2 days. Save the work.
In Food label, click Appearance and change the colours by clicking on the different colours.
Upload a digital picture of your food. This can be a picture that you have taken or one taken from an internet search. The picture loads above the Nutrition information.Save the work.
Click Export to export the label image. It should go into Nutrition Program Image Exporter. If not there may be a Firewall block or Popup block which needs to be released.
Save this image into your files. Import this image into your work.

My Diets
The Diet analysis can help you look at ways to improve your diet. You can change the ingredients and see the effect on the nutrients.
You need to complete a Diet sheet with all the foods qand drinks that you have eaten and drunk during the day. You can do this for one day or up to a week.
Click My diets and Create new diet.

4

How to use The Nutrition Program

Enter the diet name
Name - you choose, so it could be Simon.
Start day - eg Monday
Age - the age of the person whose diet you are looking at.
Sex – male or female.

- Click Add foods, and Find food.
- Type in the food you want to add to the diet – for example, toast.
- Enter the amount in grams and the time that you ate the food.
- Complete this for all the foods you ate during the day.
- Save the work.
- Look at Nutrition info and you will see three sections: 4 8 Show all.
- The 4 section shows energy, protein, carbohydrate and fat.
- The 8 section shows energy, protein, carbohydrate, total sugars, fat, saturated fat, fibre, salt, sodium.
- The Show all section has all the nutrients that are found in the diet. Click the Diet chart to show a bar chart showing data for energy, protein, carbohydrate and fat. It compares the food eaten with the daily recommendations.
- Export Nutrition Data from each of the charts and save it in your work.

Make a healthier version. Keep a copy of your original diet and try and make it healthier by clicking Make a healthier version.

My Meals
Find out how healthy a meal is. Create a recipe for the foods that are eaten at the meal. Drinks need recipes too. The program will analyse one portion of the meal for the nutritional needs of the age and sex of the person that you have chosen.

- Click Create new meals.
- Fill in the screen
- Give the meal a name
- Select the age range for the person
- Sex - male or female
- Meal Type - breakfast, Lunch or Dinner.
- Click OK if you are ready.
- Add the recipes and drinks you have created in My Recipes to the meal.
- Look at the Nutrition info. Export the Meal analysis Click Export Nutrition Data on the screen.

Nutritional recommendations
The data shown on the program should only be used as a guideline to help show if meals are too high in fat, sugar or salt. People vary in size, metabolic rate, activity levels and dietary needs. The data shown on the program is shown as an average guideline.
The meal is a part of a whole day, and whole week of eating, so snacks, drinks and other meals can contribute to our nutritional needs.

What does the chart mean?
A meal - be it breakfast, lunch or dinner can provide up to 30% of daily intake of nutrients. The meal that you put into the program will work out the nutritional value of that meal for 30% of the daily requirements for the age and sex of the person whose meal you want to analyse. The chart on the next page shows the data that we have used to calculate the requirements by age and sex. The data is based on figures provided by the School Meals Trust and the COMA report.

High energy bar - make a food label

My Recipes
This is a basic recipe for a high energy bar made from oats. This recipe is high in fat! You can adapt the recipe by adding seeds and fruit to add crunchiness and colour to the recipe. This will change the nutritional value and the cost.

High energy bar basic recipe

Ingredients
2 tablespoons golden syrup (60g)
80g brown sugar
100g margarine or butter
200g oats

Makes 16 squares

Method
1. Put the oven on at 190°C, Gas 5.
2. Heat the tablespoon over the gas or in hot water then measure the tablespoons of golden syrup.
3. In a saucepan melt the sugar, margarine and golden syrup.
4. Stir in the oats and spoon into a 22 cm square tin and smooth down.
5. Bake for 25 minutes – a bit longer if you want it crunchy.
6. Take out of the oven and mark into 16 squares. Leave to cool.

Use the Nutrition Program

- Click My Recipes and Create a new recipe.
- Enter the recipe name High energy bar, Portions 16
- In Find ingredient, find the first ingredient – golden syrup.
- Add the weight – the program helps you by giving the average weight.
- Add all the other ingredients then **save** the work.
- The recipe is saved in My Recipes.

High energy bar - make a food label

Click the Food Label section.

You need to fill in Storage info - which is information on how the product should be kept. This could be in the fridge, freezer or a cool place.
Manufactured by is the person or company who made the product.
Use by is the time when the product should be eaten, to keep it safe.

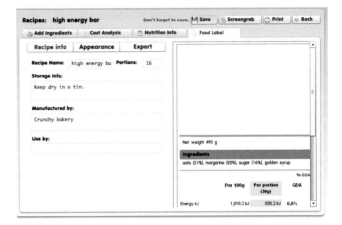

In Appearance you can upload the food picture that you want to use.
This can be a picture you have taken with a digital camera or you could use an image from the web.

In Label Style you can colour in the background and other parts of the label.

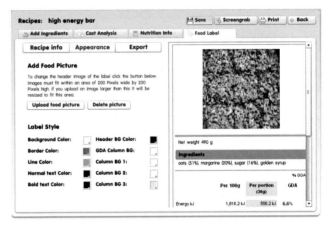

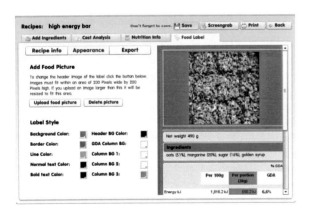

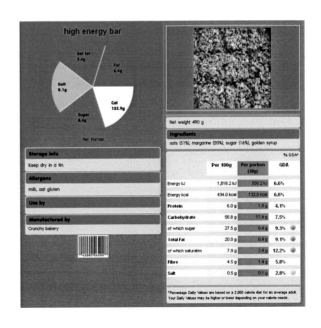

This is the label which you can export
You can see that the bar is high in sugar, fat and saturated fat, as the traffic light system is red.
This meets the nutritional target which is to design a high energy bar.
Each portion provides 132 calories.

Chilli con carne - lower the fat

My Recipes
This example shows how to lower the
amount of fat and saturated fat in a recipe.
Chilli con carne is made from minced beef,
tomatoes and red kidney beans.
The higher fat recipe is made using minced
beef and bacon and frying the onions in oil.

Chilli con carne - higher fat recipe
Serves 4
Ingredients
2 tbs oil
Onions, finely chopped 300g
Minced beef 500g
120g streaky bacon, finely chopped
1 tsp chilli powder
½ teaspoon salt
1 tablespoon tomato ketchup
400g can chopped tomatoes
400g can red kidney beans
Red pepper chopped

Method
1. Heat the oil in a large pan and add the
   onions. Cook until the onion is clear.
2. Stir in the meat and bacon and cook
   until the meat is browned.
3. Add the chilli powder, salt and ketchup
   and chopped tomatoes and bring to the
   boil.
4. Lower the heat and cook for 10 minutes
   with the lid on.
5. Add the beans and red pepper, stir and
   cook until the mixture is hot and ready
   to eat.

Lower the fat in the recipe
To lower the fat in the healthier recipe we
have
- Used 1 tablespoon of oil instead of 2.
- Used a lower fat, lean minced beef
- Removed the bacon which is quite high
  in fat and salt.

Chilli con carne - lower fat recipe
Ingredients
1 tablespoon oil
Onions, finely chopped 300g
Minced beef, lean 500g
1 tsp chilli powder
½ teaspoon salt
1 tablespoon tomato ketchup
400 g can chopped tomatoes
400 g can red kidney beans
Red pepper chopped

Is the new recipe lower in fat?
Choose the recipe and select Make a
healthier version.
The program copies the recipe and then you
change the ingredients and test it out to see
if you have lowered the fat.

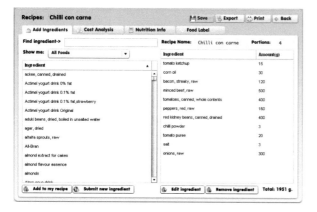

Enter the recipe details into The Nutrition
Program. You need the ingredients and the
amount in grams.

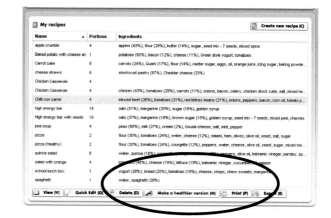

Chilli con carne - lower the fat

Chilli con carne
higher fat recipe

These are the results
The higher fat recipe contains
- 7.37g fat per 100g which is 51% of GDA

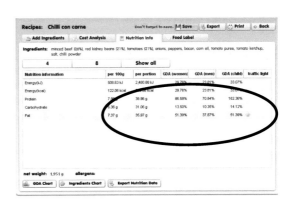

When you choose to look at the 8 Nutritional analysis section you can see the fat and saturated fat in more detail.
In the higher fat recipe there is
- 7.37g fat per 100g
- 2.5g saturated fat per 100g which is 61% GDA

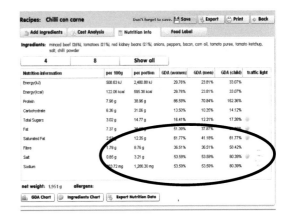

The lower fat recipe contains
- 4.32g fat per 100g which is 28% GDA
- 1.69g saturated fat per 100g which is 38% GDA.

The fat has been lowered from 7 to 4 grams in 100g
The saturated fat has been lowered from 2.5g to 1.7g.

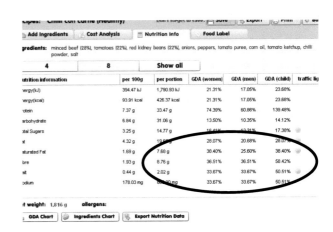

This is the food label for the healthy Chilli con carne.
You can see the amount of fat and saturated fat.
The pie chart shows that fat and saturated fat are amber which means the dish has a medium supply of fat.

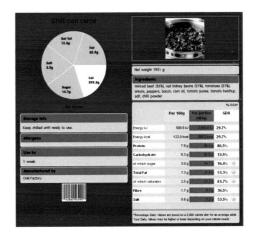

Macaroni cheese - make a healthier recipe

My recipes
In this task you will put in the ingredients for Macaroni cheese into The Nutrition Program and see its nutritional value. You can then make a healthier version to lower the fat and compare the two recipes.

Macaroni cheese
Serves 2

Ingredients
150g dried macaroni
300 ml water for cooking
300 ml milk
25g butter
25g flour
100g grated cheese
Salt and pepper
1 teaspoon Worcestershire sauce
25g grated cheese for garnish
Tomato cut into slices

Method
1. Cook the macaroni in a large pan of boiling water for 10 – 12 minutes, stirring occasionally.
2. Strain the macaroni through a colander to remove the water and put back into the saucepan.
3. Make the sauce. Put the milk, butter and flour into a small saucepan and whisk over the heat until the sauce thickens.
4. Remove from the heat and add the grated cheese then season with salt, pepper, Worcestershire sauce.
5. Stir the sauce into the macaroni and spoon into a serving dish.
6. Sprinkle on the extra grated cheese and decorate with the slices of tomato.
7. Reheat in a hot oven for 15 – 20 minutes until the top is golden.

Note – when you cook any pasta, you need to add an two times the weight of water to the recipe for analysis. This is because pasta absorbs water when it is cooked.

Macaroni cheese - make a healthier recipe

Use the Nutrition Program
Enter the ingredients into The Nutrition Program.
Fill in the chart which shows the nutrition for 100g and a portion.

This Macaroni cheese recipe is high in saturated fat, so you can try and lower the fat content by
- Changing the type of milk or cheese used
- Adding some vegetables such as leeks, peas or courgettes.
- Choosing a different fat to make the sauce with.

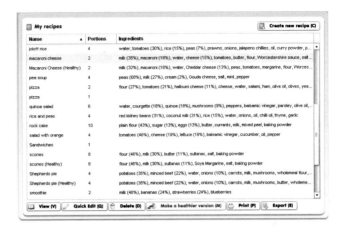

Click Make a healthier version when you have saved the first recipe.

When you add an ingredient, you can click Show me Food high in Saturated fat.
This helps you make choices of foods lower in saturated fat.

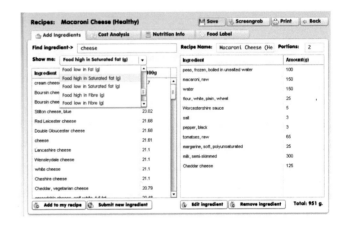

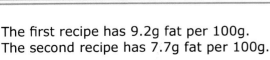

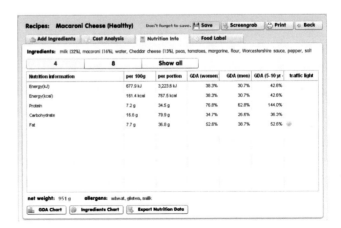

The first recipe has 9.2g fat per 100g.
The second recipe has 7.7g fat per 100g.

Tuna pasta bake - lower fat and increase the fibre

My Recipes

The aim of this worksheet is to find out how healthy the Tuna pasta bake recipe is.

Input the recipe into the Nutrition Program and find out the nutrition in 100g and a portion.

Then you change some of the ingredients to try to make a healthier recipe by lowering the fat and increasing the fibre.

Tuna pasta bake
Serves 4

Ingredients
300g dried pasta – any shape will do
750 ml water for cooking
25g flour
25g butter
600 ml milk
4 spring onions, chopped
125g frozen peas, defrosted
125g frozen sweetcorn, defrosted
2 lots of 185g tins tuna, in brine, drained
pepper
125g cheese, grated

Method
1. Cook the pasta in lots boiling water until it is soft – read the pack to get the exact cooking time. (For the nutritional analysis, the pasta absorbs two and a half times its own weight in water.) Drain the pasta.
2. Make a white sauce – put the flour, butter and milk in a saucepan and heat gently, stirring with a whisk, until the sauce thickens.
3. Mix together the spring onions, peas, sweetcorn and tuna in a bowl.
4. In a large bowl mix the pasta, sauce and vegetable and tuna mixture and pile into an oven dish.
5. Cover with grated cheese. To bake, put in the oven for 20 minutes at 190ºC, Gas 5.

Use the Nutrition Program

- Click My Recipes and Create a new recipe.
- Enter the recipe name Tuna pasta bake, Portions 4.
- In Find ingredient, find the first ingredient – pasta.
- Add the weight – the program helps you by giving the average weight.
- Add all the other ingredients then save the work.
- The recipe is saved in My Recipes.
- Click the Tuna pasta bake recipe and look at Nutrition Info.
- You will see the nutritional information for your Tuna pasta bake.

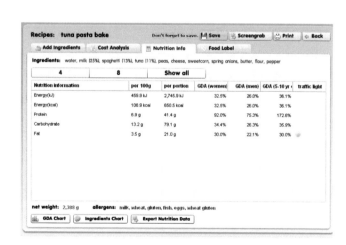

Tuna pasta bake - lower fat and increase the fibre

- In section 8 you see the traffic light for total sugars, saturated fat, and salt.
- Click the GDA chart which shows energy, protein, carbohydrate and fat.

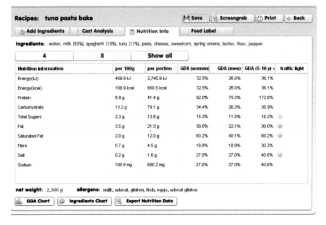

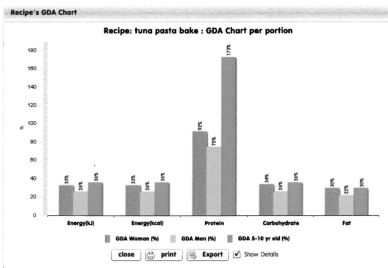

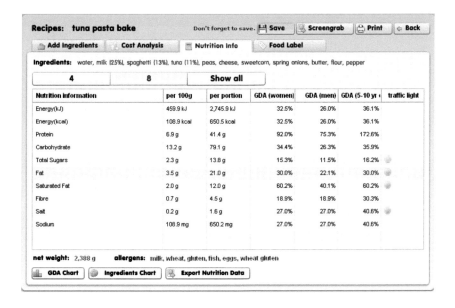

This chart shows the fat and fibre content of the Tuna Pasta bake.

Tuna pasta bake - lower fat and increase the fibre

My Recipes
Make a healthier version of your recipe.
Click Make a healthier version at the bottom of the screen.
The aim is to reduce the amount of fat and increase the fibre.

You can find foods which are high in fibre by clicking Show me and then scrolling down to find foods high in fibre that could be used.

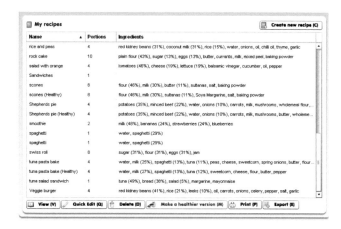

Make a healthier version

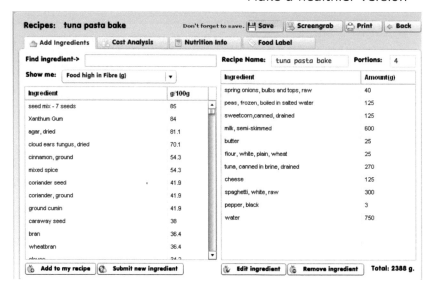

Find food high in fibre.

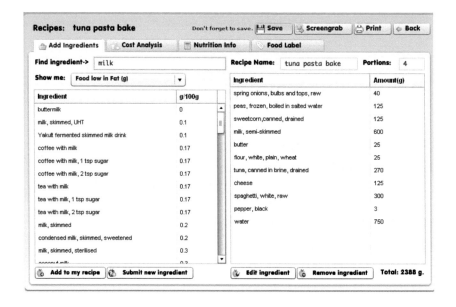

Find foods lower in fat.

Tuna pasta bake - lower fat and increase the fibre

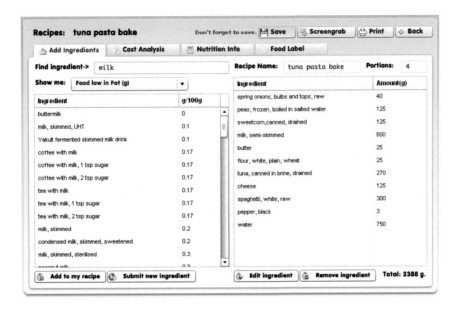

This is the new healthier version

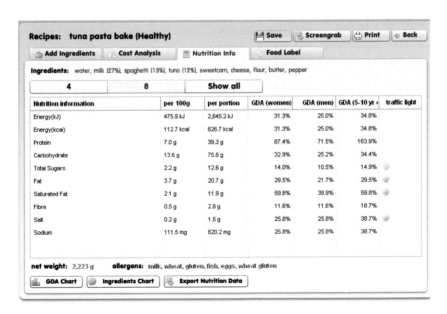

This is the nutrition for the new healthier version

Carrot cake - lower the fat

My Recipes
Design Brief
Adapt this carrot cake recipe so that it is healthier, with less fat and less saturated fat.

Carrot cake
Serves 8

Ingredients
350g carrots, peeled & grated
150g butter
200g caster sugar
3 medium eggs
200g plain flour
2 level teaspoons baking powder
½ level teaspoon mixed spice
juice of 1 orange

Topping
200g cream cheese
40g icing sugar
rind of 1 orange

Method
1. Heat the oven to 190°C, Gas 5. Grease and line a 1kg loaf tin or 20cm cake tin.
2. In a bowl mix together the oil, sugar and eggs.
3. Sieve in the flour, baking powder and mixed spice.
4. Stir in the grated carrots and juice of an orange.
5. Spoon into the tin and bake for 45 minutes until the cake is firm. Cool the cake on a wire rack.
6. For the topping, mix the cream cheese with icing sugar and orange zest and spread over the top of the cake.
7. Take a digital picture of the cake if you want to create a food label.

Lowering fat

For our health we should cut down on the amount of fat that we eat. It is important to try to replace the saturated fat we eat with unsaturated fat.

We should cut down on food that is high in saturated fat or trans fats or replace these foods with ones that are high in unsaturated fat instead.

Fats which are high in saturated fat include Butter, ghee and lard, coconut oil, coconut cream or palm oil.

In the Carrot cake you can
• Use oil instead of butter
• Use less fat in the recipe
• Replace the high fat topping with a low fat alternative such as Quark.

Nutrition analysis

Enter the ingredients into The Nutrition Program. Use a picture of the cake and insert the image to make the label,

Now work on the food label and add the picture of your cake.
You can see from the Traffic lights that the cake is high in sugar but this is normal for a cake!

Carrot cake - lower the fat

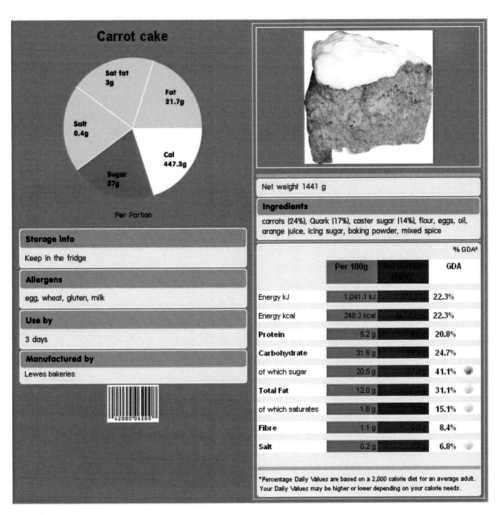

This is the new healthier recipe

To do

Put the ingredients for the carrot cake recipe into the Nutrition Program. Save the recipe and view the nutrition analysis.
Adapt the recipe by changing the fat and the topping.
Compare this recipe with the basic recipe. How has the nutrition changed?
Make a food label of the new product.
What allergens are found in the recipe?
What would be your selling price for this product?
Write 1-2 sentences to describe your product.

Pizza - lower the salt

My Recipes
Lower the salt
The easiest way to lower the salt is to add less salt and salty foods to the recipe.

This is a recipe for a very salty pizza!

Pizza recipe
Serves 2
250g strong flour
2 tbs olive oil
1 teaspoon salt
100 ml lukewarm water
2 teaspoons dried yeast
½ teaspoon sugar

Topping
200g canned, chopped tomatoes
100g grated cheese
6 slices salami
12 olives
2 slices ham

Method
1. Set the oven at 220ºC, Gas 7.
2. Put the flour, oil, salt, yeast and sugar in a bowl and stir in the warm water.Mix to a dough and turn out onto a floured board.
3. Knead the dough until smooth and elastic.
4. Grease a large baking tray and pat the dough onto the tray until it covers the base. Leave to increase in size.
5. Spoon on the chopped tomatoes and cover with grated cheese, salami, olives and strips of ham.
6. Bake for 20 minutes until well risen and golden.

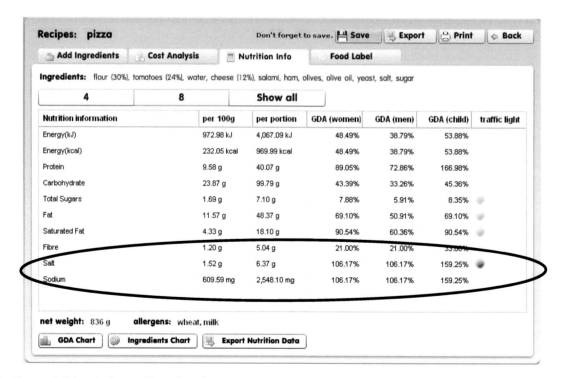

This is the nutrition information for the pizza. It has over 6 grams of salt in each portion which is the total daily allowance, so the pizza is far too high in salt.
It shows as red on the traffic light system.

Pizza - lower the salt

Lowering the salt in the pizza
In the recipe section, choose
Make a Healthier version and change the
ingredients to lower the salt.

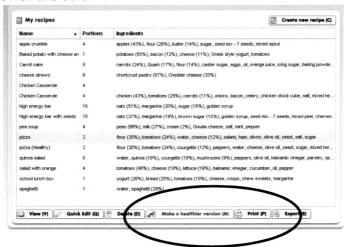

Look at the foods that are high in salt
Ham   Salami   Olives   Salt
Remove these foods and replace them with
foods with less salt but which are full of
flavour - red peppers, courgette.
Add mixed herbs to give more flavour.

Remove the salt from the pizza dough and
reduce the amount of cheese.
The new healthy pizza contains 0.55g salt a
portion – a huge reduction.
It has an amber traffic light symbol.

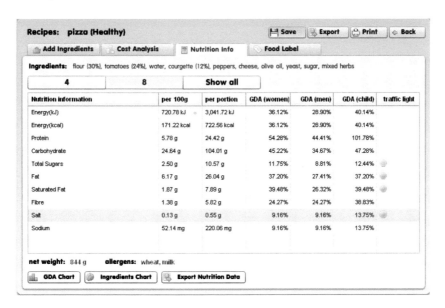

Pizza recipe Healthy
250g strong flour
2 tbs olive oil
100 ml lukewarm water
2 teaspoons dried yeast
½ teaspoon sugar

Topping
200g canned, chopped tomatoes
50g grated cheese
100g red pepper
100g courgette
½ teaspoon mixed herbs

Analyse your diet

My diets
Analyse your diet and see how good it is. Try
and improve it and see the changes.

Complete the chart to show what you have
eaten in one day.

My day's diet	
Breakfast	
Lunch	
Afternoon food	
Supper	
Snacks and drinks	

Use the Nutrition Program
- Click My Diets
- Create a new diet.
- Enter the diet name
- Start day
- Age
- Sex – you choose male or female.

Enter the foods that you have eaten. The
program helps with the weights.

Analyse your diet

Analyse your diet
- Click Diet Chart at the bottom of the screen.
- See if your diet provides for your nutrition needs.
- Click Diet Analysis Chart. This shows you other nutrients in your diet.
- Export this chart and save it onto Word, Powerpoint or Publisher.

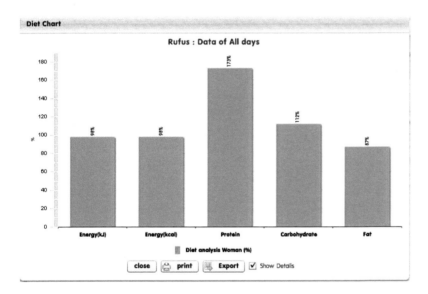

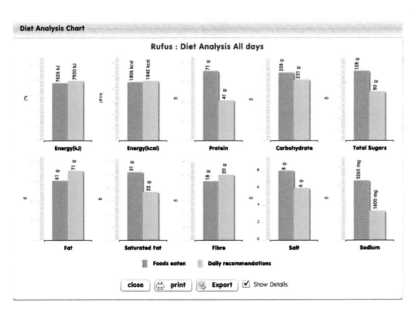

Diet analysis

Use the Diet analysis section of the Nutrition Program.

This diet is for a female, aged 15-18years. The diet lists all the foods eaten in one day and includes a roast dinner of chicken, vegetables, Yorkshire pudding and gravy.

The foods are entered with the time that they are eaten, the weight of the food eaten, then the work is saved.

Enter the foods that are eaten and the weights.

Go to Nutrition Info.
You can see from the results that the person has eaten 84% of their calorie needs, but their food provides a lot of protein and is very high in salt.

Allergens
You can see from this chart that the diet contains the following allergens:
wheat, milk, eggs, fish, gluten and soya.

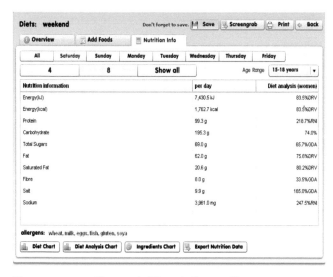

You can see the nutrition information.

If you click the Diet Chart you can see the results as a bar chart.
This shows the high intake of protein and salt.

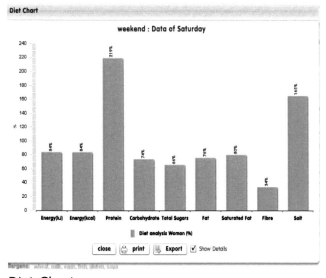

Diet Chart

Diet analysis

The Diet Analysis Chart shows a bar chart which compares the foods eaten – the orange section - with the recommended daily intake for each nutrient.
You can see the results for protein and salt (sodium) are above the recommendations. The other nutrients are just below the recommendations.

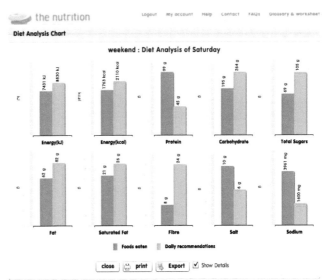

Diet Analysis Chart

The Ingredients Chart shows the foods eaten as a pie chart.

Exporting the work
You can export the work as a Screengrab. This image can be printed or copied and pasted into other work for further analysis. If you want to use the Diet Chart or the Diet Analysis Chart, click Export and the work appears on the screen ready to save.

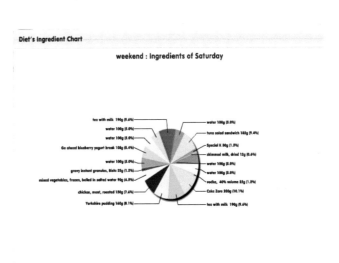

Ingredients Chart

Export work

To do
Write out a day's diet on a day when you think you ate foods high in salt or fat. Test it out on the Nutrition Program.
If the results show that the diet is too high in something, create a healthier diet.

Meal analysis - step by step

In My Meals you can find out how healthy a meal is. First you need to create a recipe for the foods that are eaten at the meal.
Drinks need recipes too.
In this example, the meal is made up of
- Chilli con carne
- Green salad
- Chocolate icecream
- Cup of coffee.

The recipes are saved and ready to use.

Meal analysis
Click Create new meals.
- Fill in the screen
- Give the meal a name
- Select the age range for the person
- Sex - male or female
- Meal Type - breakfast, Lunch or Dinner.

Click OK if you are ready.

The program will analyse one portion of the meal for the nutritional needs of the age and sex of the person that you have chosen.
So in the example, the *lunch* will be analysed for Josephine, *age 15-18* and *female*.

Add the recipes to the lunch meal.
Click the Chilli con carne, and a portion is added to the Meal section.

Complete until all the recipes, including the cup of coffee are added.
Then save.

Create new meal

Add the Chilli recipe then complete the recipes for the meal.

You are ready to look at the Nutrition info.
The Nutrition Info shows
- Nutrients per meal per person
- % of Recommended Meal Intake
- Traffic lights

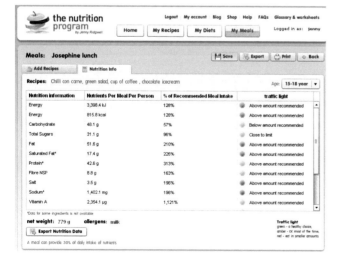

Meal analysis - step by step

Export the Meal analysis
Click Export Nutrition Data on the screen.

Josephine lunch

age: 15-18 years
sex: female
meal: lunch
recipes: Chilli con carne, green salad, cup of coffee , chocolate icecream
net weight: 779 g
allergens: milk

Nutrition Information

Nutrition	Nutrients Per Meal Per Person	% of Recommended Meal Intake	traffic light
Energy	3,398.4 kJ	128%	red : Above amount recommended
Energy	815.8 kcal	128%	red : Above amount recommended
Carbohydrate	48.1 g	57%	amber : Below amount recommended
Total Sugars	31.1 g	96%	amber : Close to limit
Fat	51.6 g	210%	red : Above amount recommended
Saturated Fat*	17.4 g	226%	red : Above amount recommended
Protein*	42.6 g	313%	amber : Above amount recommended
Fibre NSP	8.8 g	163%	amber : Above amount recommended
Salt	3.5 g	196%	red : Above amount recommended
Sodium*	1,402.1 mg	196%	red : Above amount recommended
Vitamin A	2,354.1 µg	1,121%	amber : Above amount recommended
Vitamin C	74.8 mg	534%	amber : Above amount recommended
Folate*	97.4 µg	139%	amber : Above amount recommended
Calcium*	217.3 mg	77%	amber : Below amount recommended
Iron	5.1 mg	99%	green : Close to recommended
Zinc*	6.7 mg	274%	amber : Above amount recommended

*Data for some ingredients is not available
A meal can provide 30% of daily intake of nutrients

Traffic light
green - a healthy choice,
amber - OK most of the time,
red - eat in smaller amounts

What does the chart mean?

A meal - be it breakfast, lunch or dinner can provide up to 30% of daily intake of nutrients.

The meal that you put into the program will work out the nutritional value of that meal for 30% of the daily requirements for the age and sex of the person whose meal you want to analyse.

The chart on the next page shows the data that we have used to calculate the requirements by age and sex. The data is based on figures provided by the School Meals Trust and the COMA report.

What do these things mean

A * beside the nutrients

Manufacturers do not always supply all the nutritional data for the foods that are on the database. When some data is missing you will see * beside the nutrient.

Check the recipes you have used for more information.

Traffic lights

The colours show
green - a healthy choice
amber - OK most of the time
red - eat in smaller amounts.

Meal for teenage girl rich in iron

My Meals

Task

Create a meal for a teenage girl which supplies enough iron

Find out which foods are good sources of iron. The program shows you foods which are high in iron, but many of them can't be eaten in large quantities.

These include cardamom, cumin and curry powder and you only need a tiny amount of these ingredients in a recipe. Scroll down and find foods which will be more useful.

Create a recipe.

This example shows cheese and potato pie.

Add the ingredients.

If you keep the Food high in iron clicked on it will show you the ingredients you can choose.

For the cheese and potato pie, the potatoes highest in iron are new potatoes in skins, boiled in unsalted water. It shows the amount of iron mg/100g so potatoes have 1.6 mg iron.

Choose ingredients to add more iron – for example peas.

Then save the recipe and look at the nutrition information.

What vegetables could be served for the meal? Boiled spinach is high in iron, so can be added.

Bread pudding is the dessert and served with custard.

Finally there is a cup of tea!

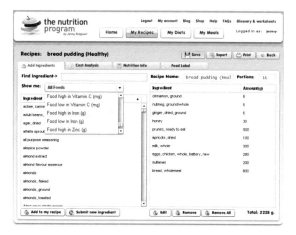

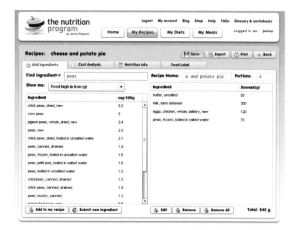

Meal for teenage girl rich in iron

Meal analysis
Click My meals and create the meal for a teenage girl for lunch. Fill in the details on screen.

The meal is

- Cheese and potato pie
- Spinach
- Bread pudding
- Custard
- Tea

Add these recipes to the meal. You have to list the recipes before you can add one portion to the meal. Save the meal and check the Nutrition info which gives the 14 nutrients.

It shows the % of the recommended meal intake and the traffic light system. The chart shows that the sugars, saturated fat and salt are too high, so the recipes need changing to make them healthier.

The task is to provide enough iron and you can see that this aim has been met.

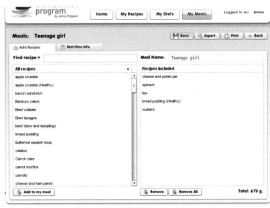

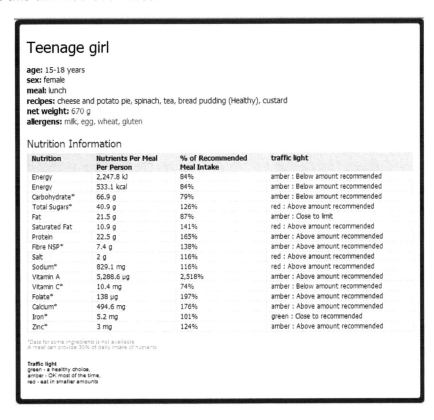

Teenage girl

age: 15-18 years
sex: female
meal: lunch
recipes: cheese and potato pie, spinach, tea, bread pudding (Healthy), custard
net weight: 670 g
allergens: milk, egg, wheat, gluten

Nutrition Information

Nutrition	Nutrients Per Meal Per Person	% of Recommended Meal Intake	traffic light
Energy	2,247.8 kJ	84%	amber : Below amount recommended
Energy	533.1 kcal	84%	amber : Below amount recommended
Carbohydrate*	66.9 g	79%	amber : Below amount recommended
Total Sugars*	40.9 g	126%	red : Above amount recommended
Fat	21.5 g	87%	amber : Close to limit
Saturated Fat	10.9 g	141%	red : Above amount recommended
Protein	22.5 g	165%	amber : Above amount recommended
Fibre NSP*	7.4 g	138%	amber : Above amount recommended
Salt	2 g	116%	red : Above amount recommended
Sodium*	829.1 mg	116%	red : Above amount recommended
Vitamin A	5,288.6 µg	2,518%	amber : Above amount recommended
Vitamin C*	10.4 mg	74%	amber : Below amount recommended
Folate*	138 µg	197%	amber : Above amount recommended
Calcium*	494.6 mg	176%	amber : Above amount recommended
Iron*	5.2 mg	101%	green : Close to recommended
Zinc*	3 mg	124%	amber : Above amount recommended

*Data for some ingredients is not available
A meal can provide 30% of daily intake of nutrients

Traffic light
green - a healthy choice,
amber - OK most of the time,
red - eat in smaller amounts

Make a vegetarian lunch

My Meals

Task

Make a vegetarian lunch for a 11 year old girl which could be served by the School Meals Service

Ideas

This vegetarian lunch includes
- Macaroni cheese
- Yogurt with fruit
- Orange juice

Create the recipes and save them
Open My meals.
Create the meal analysis for a teenage girl, for lunch.
Add the three recipes.

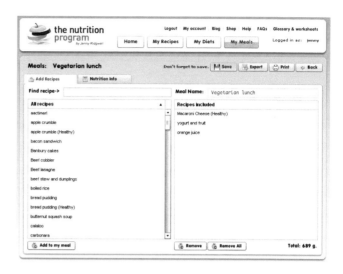

Put the recipes for the meal into My Meals

Look at the Nutrition info analysis.
This shows that the meal is very high in fat and saturated fat so the recipe for macaroni cheese must be changed.

Macaroni cheese is made from macaroni, white sauce and cheese, so look at the recipe and see how to lower the fat.
You can add vegetables such as peas and leeks.

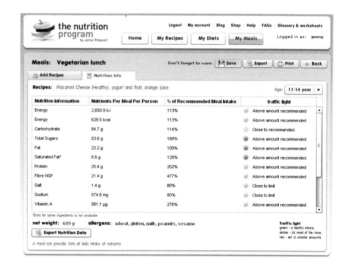

Make a vegetarian lunch

Look at the analysis.

This shows that the meal is very high in fat and saturated fat so the recipe for macaroni cheese must be changed.

The portion size has been reduced to help this and now the meal looks healthier.

Vegetarian lunch

age: 11-14 years
sex: female
meal: lunch
recipes: Macaroni Cheese (Healthy), yogurt and fruit, orange juice
net weight: 689 g
allergens: wheat, gluten, milk, peanuts, sesame

Nutrition Information

Nutrition	Nutrients Per Meal Per Person	% of Recommended Meal Intake	traffic light
Energy	2,650.9 kJ	113%	amber : Above amount recommended
Energy	628.5 kcal	113%	amber : Above amount recommended
Carbohydrate	84.7 g	114%	green : Close to recommended
Total Sugars	53.6 g	188%	red : Above amount recommended
Fat	23.2 g	109%	red : Above amount recommended
Saturated Fat*	8.6 g	129%	red : Above amount recommended
Protein	25.4 g	202%	amber : Above amount recommended
Fibre NSP	21.4 g	477%	amber : Above amount recommended
Salt	1.4 g	80%	amber : Close to limit
Sodium	574.6 mg	80%	amber : Close to limit
Vitamin A	581.1 µg	276%	amber : Above amount recommended
Vitamin C*	174.7 mg	1,426%	amber : Above amount recommended
Folate	152.5 µg	217%	amber : Above amount recommended
Calcium	572.5 mg	204%	amber : Above amount recommended
Iron	1.9 mg	37%	amber : Below amount recommended
Zinc	2.8 mg	90%	green : Close to recommended

*Data for some ingredients is not available
A meal can provide 30% of daily intake of nutrients

Traffic light
green - a healthy choice,
amber - OK most of the time,
red - eat in smaller amounts

The meal has been changed and now looks much healthier but the saturated fat is still slightly too high.

If vegetables were served with this meal, and the portion of macaroni cheese was smaller, this would lower the fat content.

To do
Plan a vegetarian lunch with two courses. Choose an age group and see how healthy it is.
Write some comments on your results and compare your results with others.

Make a healthy packed lunch

My Meals
Task

Make a healthy packed lunch

Try and choose a healthy packed lunch for the following people

- A 7 year old boy

- A 14 year old girl

- A 16 year old boy

- A 25 year old woman

- A 40 year old man.

To do

Recipes

Create recipes for the packed lunch.

Choose a sandwich such as cheese and pickle and create the recipe in My Recipes.

Sandwich ingredients

- 2 slices of bread,

- butter or spread,

- cheese,

- pickle.

Save the recipe.

You might want to include some crisps, fruit and a drink so you need to create recipes for these. The easiest way is to call them Extras and then add the things that you have chosen such as an apple.

Something sweet

You might include yogurt or a recipe such as bread pudding. Again, create the recipe and save it.

My meals

Open my meals and select the age for the person you are designing the packed lunch for. We are choosing a 16 year old boy.

Choose the recipes that you want for the packed lunch.

It could be

- Cheese and pickle sandwich

- Crisps, apple and orange juice

- Bread pudding.

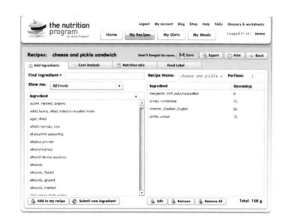

Create the recipe for the sandwich.

Add the recipes to the Meals

Make a healthy packed lunch

- Test the nutritional value of the packed lunch.

Does it provide 30% of the daily needs for that person?

If not make changes to the portion sizes or the recipe.

Test out the packed lunch for the other people. As people get older their nutritional needs change so you may have to include more or less items in the packed lunch.

Further work

Here are some packed lunch recipes that you can test out to see how healthy they are. Look up the recipes on the internet and add them to a packed lunch.

- Cheese and onion flan
- Coleslaw
- Samosas
- Chicken sandwich with salad
- Fruit salad

To do

1. Create a really unhealthy packed lunch – save it into your work and show why it is so unhealthy.

2. Create 3 lots of healthy packed lunch which could be shown to parents of primary school children.

3. Create your favourite packed lunch and explain why you like it.

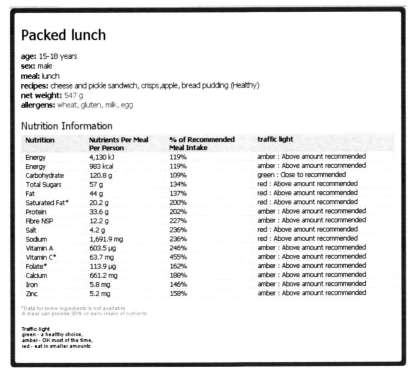

Packed lunch

age: 15-18 years
sex: male
meal: lunch
recipes: cheese and pickle sandwich, crisps,apple, bread pudding (Healthy)
net weight: 547 g
allergens: wheat, gluten, milk, egg

Nutrition Information

Nutrition	Nutrients Per Meal Per Person	% of Recommended Meal Intake	traffic light
Energy	4,130 kJ	119%	amber : Above amount recommended
Energy	983 kcal	119%	amber : Above amount recommended
Carbohydrate	120.8 g	109%	green : Close to recommended
Total Sugars	57 g	134%	red : Above amount recommended
Fat	44 g	137%	red : Above amount recommended
Saturated Fat*	20.2 g	200%	red : Above amount recommended
Protein	33.6 g	202%	amber : Above amount recommended
Fibre NSP	12.2 g	227%	amber : Above amount recommended
Salt	4.2 g	236%	red : Above amount recommended
Sodium	1,691.9 mg	236%	red : Above amount recommended
Vitamin A	603.5 µg	246%	amber : Above amount recommended
Vitamin C*	63.7 mg	455%	amber : Above amount recommended
Folate*	113.9 µg	162%	amber : Above amount recommended
Calcium	661.2 mg	188%	amber : Above amount recommended
Iron	5.8 mg	146%	amber : Above amount recommended
Zinc	5.2 mg	158%	amber : Above amount recommended

*Data for some ingredients is not available
A meal can provide 30% of daily intake of nutrients

Traffic light
green - a healthy choice,
amber - OK most of the time,
red - eat in smaller amounts

Look at the results and find out how well you have done.

Meal for £5

My Meals

Task
Design a healthy meal for four people that will cost £5.

Firstly, carry out some research to find out which foods are expensive and which are better value.

Foods like rump steak and types of fish can be expensive.

Choose inexpensive foods with high nutritional value such as eggs, cheese, peas, beans and lentils and buy seasonal fruits and vegetables to keep in budget.

Create your recipes.

This is the choice

- Chilli con carne
- Boiled rice
- Apple crumble
- Custard.

Look at the costing of each recipe and write down the total cost.

You may disagree with some of the prices which may vary in your area. If so, click the Edit button and change them. You can check prices on supermarket shelves on the internet.

In this example, the total meal costs £4.93.

If your meal is within the £5 budget you can proceed to see if it is healthy. If it costs more than £5 make some changes.Go to My Meals.

Choose the average age for the people you are designing for.

For example if it is two parents (aged 40) and two teenagers (15), the average age is 28 years. Choose male or female.

This is the costing for Chilli con carne

This is the costing for Apple crumble - you can edit the cost.

This is the costing for Boiled rice

Meal for £5

Enter the recipes into your meal and save. Save the meal and look at the Nutrition info.

In this example when all the recipes have been added, you can see that the meal provides more calories (energy) than is needed, so the portion sizes need to be reduced. Go back to the recipes and change something – in this case, the amount of meat in the Chilli con carne is reduced. The portion sizes of all the recipes need to be looked at as the meal supplies too much food, so these have been changed. Analyse the results.

The four meals are added to My Meals

The final meal meets the targets, but the amount of salt in the meal as it is too high. This screen shows the final analysis of the meal which is quite healthy.

My Meals shows the nutritional analysis

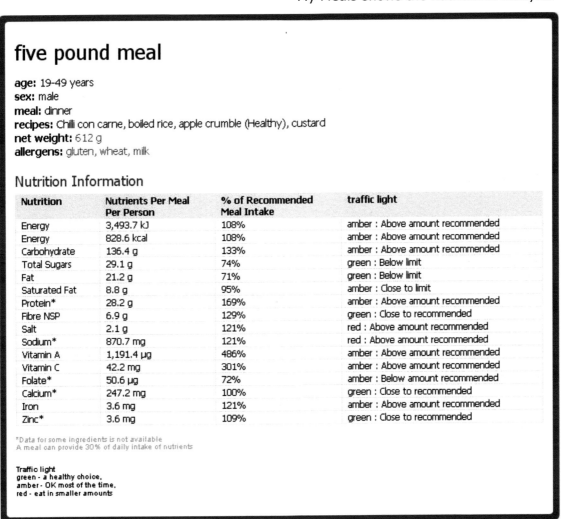

five pound meal

age: 19-49 years
sex: male
meal: dinner
recipes: Chilli con carne, boiled rice, apple crumble (Healthy), custard
net weight: 612 g
allergens: gluten, wheat, milk

Nutrition Information

Nutrition	Nutrients Per Meal Per Person	% of Recommended Meal Intake	traffic light
Energy	3,493.7 kJ	108%	amber : Above amount recommended
Energy	828.6 kcal	108%	amber : Above amount recommended
Carbohydrate	136.4 g	133%	amber : Above amount recommended
Total Sugars	29.1 g	74%	green : Below limit
Fat	21.2 g	71%	green : Below limit
Saturated Fat	8.8 g	95%	amber : Close to limit
Protein*	28.2 g	169%	amber : Above amount recommended
Fibre NSP	6.9 g	129%	green : Close to recommended
Salt	2.1 g	121%	red : Above amount recommended
Sodium*	870.7 mg	121%	red : Above amount recommended
Vitamin A	1,191.4 µg	486%	amber : Above amount recommended
Vitamin C	42.2 mg	301%	amber : Above amount recommended
Folate*	50.6 µg	72%	amber : Below amount recommended
Calcium*	247.2 mg	100%	green : Close to recommended
Iron	3.6 mg	121%	amber : Above amount recommended
Zinc*	3.6 mg	109%	green : Close to recommended

*Data for some ingredients is not available
A meal can provide 30% of daily intake of nutrients

Traffic light
green - a healthy choice.
amber - OK most of the time.
red - eat in smaller amounts

Make a healthy breakfast

A breakfast is an important meal of the day as you are breaking your fast.

My Meals

Task
Come up with a menu for a healthy breakfast for a teenage boy.

In this example, the choice is:

- Porridge with milk and sugar
- Beans and bacon on wholemeal toast
- Tea with milk.

First create the recipes in My Recipes.

Porridge is made from
Oats cooked in water and served with milk and sugar.
Enter each of these ingredients into My Recipes and save it.

Now create the other recipes for
Beans and bacon on wholemeal toast
Tea with milk.

The reason you need separate recipes for a cup of tea is that you may make your tea to a different recipe.
You could use skimmed milk or whole milk, and add sugar or sweetener.
These ingredients will all change the nutritional value of the tea.

Save all the recipes ready for the next section.

My meals
For My meals chose the age, sex and meal

In My recipes add all the ingredients that make up the recipe such as porridge.

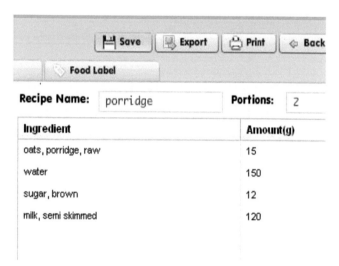

In My recipes add all the ingredients that make up the recipe such as porridge.

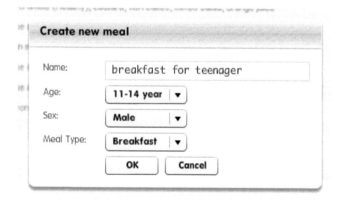

For My meals chose the age, sex and meal type, in this case breakfast.

Make a healthy breakfast

type, in this case Breakfast.

Select the recipes that you want and a portion of each is added to My Meals. Save the work.

The program tells you that you are adding one portion of the recipe that you have chosen.

The program tells you that you are adding one portion of the recipe.

This shows that the porridge, beans and bacon on toast and tea have been added to the meal.

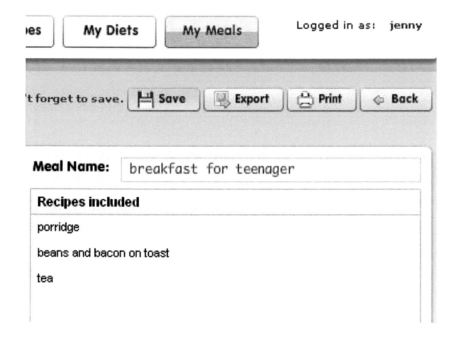

Make a healthy breakfast

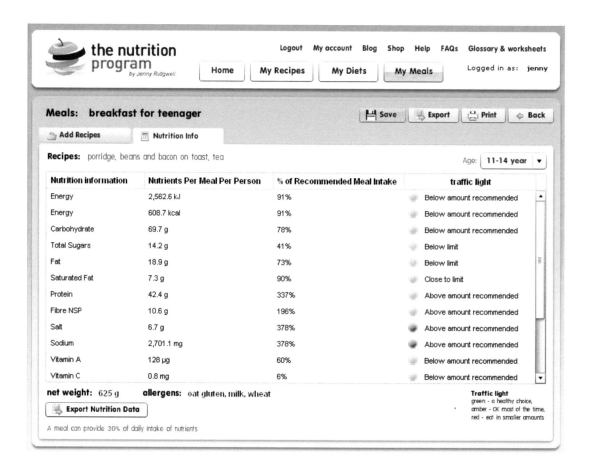

Look at the Nutrition info.

This shows the range of 14 nutrients under Nutrients per meal per person

It also shows the % or recommended meal intake.

Then the traffic light system which warns if the meal is not healthy enough.

You can also see the net weight.

And the allergens which in this case are oat gluten, milk and wheat.

Export the Nutrition data so that you see all the information.

To do
Plan a healthy breakfast. Choose an age group and see how healthy it is.
Write some comments on your results and compare your results with others.
If needed, add some more foods to improve the breakfast.

Make a healthy breakfast

What do the results of the breakfast mean?

Remember that this breakfast is one of several snacks and meals eaten during the day. People often don't like to eat a large breakfast, and may prefer a slightly larger meal at lunchtime or in the evening.

Breakfast provides you with energy to start the day and helps concentration. A healthy breakfast provides you with essential nutrients to keep your body healthy.

Analysis of results

This breakfast provides 91% of meal intake which is OK and a little more could be eaten.

The carbohydrate is below the amount recommended, so more toast could be included.

The sugars and fat are below the limit which is good.

The saturated fat is close to the limit, due to the bacon.

Protein is high, but for a teenage boy this is OK.

Fibre is high which is good for your digestive system.

Salt is above the recommended limit so look at the salt in bacon or baked beans.

The minerals and vitamins are close to recommended amount except for vitamins A and C. If the breakfast contained a glass of orange juice, then this would increase the vitamin C content.

breakfast for teenager

age: 11-14 years
sex: male
meal: breakfast
recipes: porridge, beans and bacon on toast, tea
net weight: 625 g
allergens: oat gluten, milk, wheat

Nutrition Information

Nutrition	Nutrients Per Meal Per Person	% of Recommended Meal Intake	traffic light
Energy	2,562.6 kJ	91%	amber : Below amount recommended
Energy	608.6 kcal	91%	amber : Below amount recommended
Carbohydrate	69.7 g	78%	amber : Below amount recommended
Total Sugars	14.2 g	41%	green : Below limit
Fat	18.9 g	73%	green : Below limit
Saturated Fat	7.3 g	90%	amber : Close to limit
Protein	42.4 g	337%	amber : Above amount recommended
Fibre NSP	10.6 g	196%	amber : Above amount recommended
Salt	6.7 g	378%	red : Above amount recommended
Sodium	2,701.1 mg	378%	red : Above amount recommended
Vitamin A	128 µg	60%	amber : Below amount recommended
Vitamin C	0.8 mg	6%	amber : Below amount recommended
Folate	64.9 µg	92%	green : Close to recommended
Calcium	232.7 mg	66%	amber : Below amount recommended
Iron	3.8 mg	96%	green : Close to recommended
Zinc	3.6 mg	115%	green : Close to recommended

A meal can provide 30% of daily intake of nutrients

Traffic light
green - a healthy choice,
amber - OK most of the time,
red - eat in smaller amounts

Meal analysis - how to use

What do the results tell us about Josephine's lunch?

Energy is 128% which may mean the portions are too big.

The total weight of the meal is 779g - a lot.

Fat and saturated fat are very high and show red in the traffic light system.

To make changes:
- reduce the portion sizes
- look at the recipes to see how you can lower the fat and make a healthier version.

Salt (sodium) are very high, so change the recipes to lower the salt.

This chart shows the traffic light boundaries used for each nutrient for the total meal.

Nutritional recommendations

The data shown on the program should only be used as a guideline to help show if meals are too high in fat, sugar or salt.

People vary in size, metabolic rate, activity levels and dietary needs.

The data shown on the program is shown as an average guideline.

But remember that the meal is a part of a whole day, and whole week of eating, so snacks, drinks and other meals can contribute to our nutritional needs.

	green	amber	red
comments			'above amount recommended'.
Energy kJ / kcal	in between 95% below and up to 105%	below 95% 105-120% above	120% above recommended
Carbohydrate g	in between 90% and up to 120%	below 90% if above 120%	
Total sugars g	below 80%	80-100%	if above 100%
Fat g	below 80%	80-100%	if above 100%
Saturated fat	below 80%	80-100%	if above 100%
Protein	90- 120%	below 90% if above 120%	
Fibre NSP	in between 90% and up to 130%	below 90% if above 130%	
Salt g	below 80%	80-100%	if above 100%
Vitamin A ug	in between 90% and up to 120%	if 90% and below if above 120%	
Vitamin C mg	in between 90% and up to 120%	if 90% and below if above 120%	
Folate ug	in between 90% and up to 120%	if 90% and below if above 120%	
Calcium mg	in between 90% and up to 120%	if 90% and below if above 120%	
Iron mg	in between 90% and up to 120%	if 90% and below if above 120%	
Zinc mg	in between 90% and up to 120%	if 90% and below if above 120%	

Meal analysis - how to use

This chart shows the data that is used for the Meals analysis in the program

Nutrient	Min or max	4-6 male	4-6 female	7-10 male	7-10 female	11 to 14 male	11 to 14 female	15-18 male	15-18 female	19-49 male	19-49 female	50-64 male	50-64 female	65+ male	65+ female
Energy kj	max EAR	2148	1938	2472	2184	2781	2376	3453	2649	3180	2430	2979	2397	2631	2283
kcal	EAR	515	463	588	522	666	554	826	633	765	582	714	570	630	543
Carbohydrate g	Min	69	61.8	79	69.6	89	73.8	110	84.4	102	77.6	98.6	76	88.5	74
Total sugars	Max	25	25	28.5	28.5	34.1	28.5	42.4	32.4	39.2	29.9	36.6	29.2	32.4	27.8
Fat g	Max	20	18	23	20.3	25.9	21.3	32	24.6	29.7	22.6	28.8	22.6	25.8	21.6
Saturated fat g	Max	6.3	5.6	7.2	6.3	8.1	6.7	10.1	7.7	9.3	7.1	9	7	8.1	6.8
Protein g	Min RNI	5.91	5.91	8.5	8.5	12.6	12.6	16.6	13.6	16.7	13.5	16	14	16	14
Fibre NSP g	Min	4.2	3.6	4.8	4.2	5.4	4.5	5.4	5.4	5.4	5.4	5.4	5.4	5.4	5.4
salt g	max SACN	0.9	0.9	1.5	1.5	1.8	1.8	1.8	1.8	1.8	1.8	1.8	1.8	1.8	1.8
sodium mg	max SACN	357	357	595	595	714	714	714	714	714	714	714	714	714	714
Vitamin A ug	Min RNI	140	140	175	175	210	210	245	210	245	210	245	210	245	210
Vitamin C mg	Min RNI	10.5	10.5	10.5	10.5	12.25	12.25	14	14	14	14	14	14	14	14
Folate ug	Min RNI	35	35	52.5	52.5	70	70	70	70	70	70	70	70	70	70
Calcium mg	Min RNI	158	158	193	193	350	280	350	280	245	245	245	245	245	245
Iron mg	Min RNI	2.1	2.1	3	3	4	5.2	4	5.2	3	3	3	3	3	3
Zinc mg	Min RNI	2.3	2.3	2.45	2.45	3.15	3.15	3.3	2.45	3.3	2.45	3.3	2.45	3.3	2.45
EAR	Estimated average requirement														
RNI	Reference Nutrient Intake														
SACN	Scientific Advisory Committee on Nutrition														

Meal analysis - how to use

Minimum levels are set for these nutrients because too little can be harmful: Carbohydrate, Protein, Fibre, Vitamin A, Vitamin C, folate, calcium, iron, and zinc.

Maximum levels are set for these nutrients because too much can be harmful:
sodium - shown as salt
fat and saturated fat
NMES - we do not have NMES data available for many foods, so have shown Total sugars.

Food energy (or energy from food) comes from carbohydrate, fat and protein and should be in the following proportions:
- not less than 50% from carbohydrate
- not more than 11% from NMES
- not more than 35% from fat
- not more than 11% from saturated fat
- protein.

The meal analysis investigates 14 nutrients which are considered important in our diets.

Carbohydrates
There are two types of carbohydrate – starches and sugars.
Starchy carbohydrates should provide the main source of energy in the diet and should form the main component of a meal.

Sources of starchy carbohydrate
Bread of all types, rice, pasta, noodles, potatoes, yam, oats, cassava, couscous, breakfast cereals, wheat grains like bulgar wheat, lentils, red kidney beans and black eye beans.

Food and drink high in NME sugars often provide calories but few other essential nutrients.
A diet high in NME sugars contributes to tooth decay.

Sources of NME sugars
Table sugar, jam, honey, sweetened drinks, cakes, pastries, ice cream, sweets, biscuits, confectionery and chocolate.

Fat
Fat has more than twice the calories weight for weight of carbohydrate. It is a concentrated source of energy and provides essential fatty acids.

High fat intake can lead to excess energy intake and weight gain.

Sources of fat
Butter, lard, margarine, fat spreads, oils or dressings such as mayonnaise, chips and other deep-fried food, potato waffles, garlic bread, pastries, cakes, biscuits, creamy puddings, meat or meat products such as pasties.

There are two types of fat
Saturated fat comes mainly from animals
Unsaturated fat comes mainly from plants and fish.
A diet high in saturated fat can cause high cholesterol levels and increase the risk of diseases such as coronary heart disease, diabetes and some cancers.

Sources of saturated fat
Butter, lard, some margarine, cream, coconut oil or cream, palm oil, mayonnaise, salad cream, meat products (e.g. pies, burgers or sausages), hard cheeses (e.g. cheddar), cakes or biscuits.

Protein is important for the growth and repair of body tissues like muscles. School students are growing fast so protein is particularly important for them.

Sources of protein
Meat, fish, milk, cheese, eggs, yoghurt, nuts* and seeds, red kidney beans, chickpeas, lentils, cereals and meat alternatives (e.g. tofu).

Fibre is essential for a healthy digestive system. It assists bowel function and prevents problems such as constipation.

Meal analysis - how to use

Sources of fibre
Brown rice, oats, wholegrain cereals, muesli, potatoes with skins, wholemeal pasta, wholemeal bread, bulgar wheat, lentils, chickpeas, red kidney beans, fruit and vegetables.

Sodium is a component of salt.
Salt is needed to maintain fluid balance in the body and for nerve and muscle function. Too much salt can cause high blood pressure, which may lead to a stroke, heart disease and kidney problems.

Sources of sodium
Ready made soups and sauces, gravy, processed food, some breakfast cereals, salty snacks (e.g. crisps and salted nuts), bacon, ham, sausages, pizza, cheese and condiments.

Vitamin A is important for growth and tissue repair, good eyesight and the immune system.

Sources of vitamin A
Oily fish, eggs, liver, cheese, butter and milk.
Yellow, orange and red coloured fruits and veg such as carrots, peppers, apricots, oranges, butternut squash, sweet potato, tomatoes and dark green leafy vegetables.

Vitamin C is needed for wound healing and the structure of blood vessels and skin. Vitamin C is an antioxidant which helps to protect the body from infections and disease. Vitamin C enhances iron absorption.

Sources of vitamin C
Fruits – especially citrus fruits (oranges, lemons, limes, grapefruit), berries and kiwi fruits.
Vegetables (including frozen) – especially broccoli, green and red

Folate is essential for blood cells, the nervous system and helps prevent anaemia. It is particularly important in the early stages of pregnancy as it helps to protect the baby from neural tube defects such as spina bifida.

Sources of folate
Liver, yeast extract, orange juice, green leafy vegetables (e.g. spinach), green beans, beetroot, chickpeas, black-eye beans, broccoli, peas and brown rice. Breakfast cereals are fortified with folate.

Calcium is essential for strong bones and teeth, especially during childhood and adolescence when the skeleton is growing. It is also important for muscle and nerve function as well as blood clotting. Pupils with low calcium are at risk of developing osteoporosis or brittle bones in later life.

Sources of calcium
Dairy products such as milk, cheese, yoghurt, canned fish with bones (e.g. salmon and pilchards), broccoli, cabbage, dried fruits, tofu, red kidney beans, chickpeas and soya beans. White and brown bread are fortified with calcium.

Iron is needed for the production of red blood cells which carry oxygen around the body. Iron plays an important role in maintaining a healthy immune system. It is especially important for teenage girls. Iron deficiency can cause anaemia which may result in headaches and insomnia.

Sources of iron
Red meat, offal (especially liver and kidney), canned fish, eggs, dark green leafy vegetables, peas, wholegrains (e.g. brown rice), nuts and seeds, red kidney beans, black-eye beans, lentils, chickpeas, dried apricots and raisins.

Zinc has a number of important functions, including growth and tissue repair, wound healing and the immune system.

Sources of zinc
Red meat, offal (especially liver and kidney), eggs, fish, milk and other dairy products, cereals, red kidney beans, soya products, lentils, chickpeas and nuts.

Details taken from Nutrition based standards School Food Trust.

GCSE and A/S level tasks

These are some Meal analysis tasks for GCSE

1. Create a lunch for a teenage girl. Make sure that the meal supplies enough iron for her needs. Show which foods are good sources of iron in this meal.

2. Make a breakfast for a hungry teenage boy. Show how you have supplied enough protein in the meal, and a good supply of vitamin C, calcium and iron.

3. A recent survey found that 74% of school meals consumed by girls aged 11–18 did not contain enough folate. Your task is to prepare a meal for this group and show how you have supplied enough folate.

4. A recent survey found that 80% of school meals eaten by boys aged 11–18 and 77% of school meals eaten by girls aged 11–18 did not contain enough calcium. Your task is to prepare a meal for this group and show how you have supplied enough calcium.

5. A recent survey found that 79% of school meals eaten by boys aged 11–18 did not contain enough fibre. Your task is to prepare a meal for this group and show how you have supplied enough fibre.

6. A recent survey found that 76% of school meals eaten by boys aged 11–18 contained too much fat. Your task is to prepare a meal for this group and show how you have not supplied too much fat.

A/S FOOD TECHNOLOGY ASSIGNMENTS
Students need to do research to find good sources of different nutrients, design recipes that meet the given criteria, make them and justify the results. They can also make a recipe card, showing the ingredients, method of making and nutritional information.
MAKING

- Plan and make a nutritionally balanced one dish main meal.
- Apply your knowledge of hygiene, safety and quality control throughout the making process.
- Display and photograph your product.
RECIPE CARD

Produce an attractive recipe card that should include:
- A photograph of the finished dish.
- List ingredients and quantities.
- Clear step by step instructions for making the dish.
- Provide nutritional analysis and information for a serving and a 100g (you will need to use the Nutrition Program).
- Include a range of modifications.

Tasks
1. Research the nutritional needs of your chosen dietary group.
- What might influence their dietary choices and opinions?
- What are their nutritional needs (DRV'S) and why?
- What recommendations would you make to ensure they meet their needs?
- Plan a 2 day menu for them and justify your choices.
- Present your findings to the group.
2. Keep a food diary of everything you eat and drink for 3 days.
- Analyse your food diary using www.nutritionprogram.co.uk.
- Present your nutrient intake using tables, charts and graphs.
- Discuss if your diet is healthy and balanced and explain why.
- What implications might this have on your long term health?
- Suggest ways to improve your diet.

3. Plan and make a savoury main course dish that will:

- provide your daily requirement of protein
- contribute to five a day
- contain less than 20g total fat and less than 10g saturated fat

My thanks to J Chaffey for this work.
Further sources of information:
www.nutrition.org.uk
www.food.gov.uk

Worksheets for the Nutrition Program

This series of worksheets will help you get started with activities to use The Nutrition Program.

The Worksheets

- Getting started with a smoothie
- Tuna pasta bake - lower the fat and increase the fibre
- Make a healthier scones recipe
- Veggie burger versus Beef burger
- Spaghetti with bacon and cream - lower the fat
- Macaroni cheese - change the recipe
- Pizza - lower the salt
- High energy bar - make a food label
- Couscous salad - looking at allergens
- Carrot cake – costing and nutrition
- School lunch - compare four lunches
- Your diet
- Nutrition Crossword, Quick Quiz

The skills shown are:
- recipe analysis
- changing the nutrition of a recipe
- comparing recipe nutrition
- looking at allergens
- costing a recipe
- diet and lunchbox analysis.

The Worksheets

Getting started with a smoothie
This activity shows step by step how to put a recipe into the program.

Tuna pasta bake
Lower the fat and increase the fibre.
This activity shows how to work out the nutritional value of a recipe then change it to make it healthier and lower the fat and increase the fibre.

Make a healthier scones recipe
This activity shows how to adapt a scone recipe to increase the fibre.

Veggie burger versus Beef burger
Compare the nutrition.
This activity compares two recipes to look at their nutritional value.

Spaghetti with bacon and cream - lower the fat
This activity takes a very fatty recipe and looks at ways to lower the fat to make it more healthy.

Macaroni cheese
Change the recipe and lower the fat and increase the fibre.

Pizza - lower the salt
This activity shows a recipe for a very salty pizza and then you can make another one with a much lower salt content.

High energy oat bar
Make a food label and then look at changing the nutrition.

Couscous salad
Look at allergens.
This activity tells you about allergens and how to make a recipe allergen free.

Carrot cake – costing and nutrition
This activity shows how to look at the cost of making a product and then how to change the costs. This will help to design within budget limits and to help work out a selling price.

School lunch - compare four lunches
Using the diet section, compare 4 lunches to see which is the healthiest then design your own.

Your diet
Analyse your diet and see how good it is. Try and improve it and see the changes.

Nutrition Crossword
To test your knowledge - with answers!

Getting started with a smoothie

My Recipes
In this worksheet, you will put a simple recipe into The Nutrition Program and look at the cost and nutrition information that the program provides.

Smoothie recipe
Serves 2

Ingredients
100g strawberries
1 medium banana
200 ml semi skimmed milk
10 blueberries

Method
1. Take the stalk out of the strawberries, and peel and chop the banana.
2. Place all the ingredients in a food processor and whizz until smooth.
3. Serve and drink immediately.

Use the Nutrition Program

- Click My Recipes and Create a new recipe.
- Enter the recipe name Smoothie, Portions 2.
- In Find ingredient, find the first ingredient – strawberries.
- Add the weight – the program helps you by giving the average weight.
- Add all the other ingredients then save the work.
- The recipe is saved in My Recipes.
- Click the Smoothie and look at Nutrition Info.
- You will see the nutritional information for your Smoothie.

| 4 | 8 | Show all |

Getting started with a smoothie

To do
Put the recipe into the program and look
at the Cost Analysis and the Nutrition
info and export the work.
What is the nutrition for 100g of the
main 8 nutrients?
Complete the chart for the smoothie.

Smoothie 1		
	100g	portion
Energy kcal		
Protein		
Carbohydrate		
Fat		
Saturated fat		
Fibre		
Salt		

Now change the recipe and add different
ingredients. How does the nutrition for
100g change?
Write out the new recipe and complete
the nutrition chart or export the chart
from the program.

Smoothie 2		
	100g	portion
Energy kcal		
Protein		
Carbohydrate		
Fat		
Saturated fat		
Fibre		
Salt		

My smoothie recipe

Tuna pasta bake - lower the fat and increase the fibre

My Recipes

The aim of this worksheet is to find out how healthy the Tuna pasta bake recipe is.

Input the recipe into the Nutrition Program and find out the nutrition in 100g and a portion.

Then you change some of the ingredients to try to make a healthier recipe by lowering the fat and increasing the fibre.

Tuna pasta bake
Serves 4

Ingredients
300g dried pasta – any shape will do
750 ml water for cooking
25g flour
25g butter
600 ml milk
4 spring onions, chopped
125g frozen peas, defrosted
125g frozen sweetcorn, defrosted
2 lots of 185 g tins tuna, in brine, drained
pepper
125g cheese, grated

Method
1. Cook the pasta in lots boiling water until it is soft – read the pack to get the exact cooking time. (For the nutritional analysis, the pasta absorbs two and a half times its own weight in water.) Drain the pasta.
2. Make a white sauce – put the flour, butter and milk in a saucepan and heat gently, stirring with a whisk, until the sauce thickens.
3. Mix together the spring onions, peas, sweetcorn and tuna in a bowl.
4. In a large bowl mix the pasta, sauce and vegetable and tuna mixture and pile into an oven dish.
5. Cover with grated cheese. To bake, put in the oven for 20 minutes at 190ºC, Gas Mark 5.

Use the Nutrition Program

- Click My Recipes and Create a new recipe.
- Enter the recipe name Tuna pasta bake, Portions 4.
- In Find ingredient, find the first ingredient – pasta.
- Add the weight – the program helps you by giving the average weight.
- Add all the other ingredients then save the work.
- The recipe is saved in My Recipes.
- Click the Tuna pasta bake recipe and look at Nutrition Info.

- You will see the nutritional information for your Tuna pasta bake.

| 4 | 8 | Show all |

Click the 4 section - Can you see the traffic light for fat? What is the colour?
- In section 8 you see the traffic light for total sugars, saturated fat, and salt.
- Click the GDA chart which shows energy, protein, carbohydrate and fat.

Tuna Pasta bake - lower the fat and increase the fibre

To do
Use the Nutrition Program to fill in the
chart and complete the questions below.

Tuna pasta bake		
	100g	portion
Energy kcal		
Protein		
Carbohydrate		
Fat		
Saturated fat		
Fibre		
Salt		

1.   What type of milk did you use in the recipe? ....

2.   What type of cheese did you use?   ....

3.   What type of flour did you use?   ....

4.   What changes could you make to the recipe to lower the fat?

        ....

5.   What changes could you make to the recipe to increase the fibre?

        ....

Make a healthier scones recipe

My Recipes
The aim of this task is to take a basic recipe such as scones, work out the nutrition, then change it to make it more healthy – in this case, higher in fibre and lower in fat.

Scone recipe - plain scones
8 scones

Ingredients
200g self raising white flour
3g salt
3g baking powder
50g butter
150 ml milk
beaten egg

Method
1. Set the oven at 220°C / Gas 7.
2. Sieve the flour, salt and baking powder into a mixing bowl. Rub in the butter using your fingertips until the mixture looks like breadcrumbs.
3. Pour in the milk and mix to form a soft dough. Knead gently and roll out to 2.5cm and cut into 8 scones using a cutter.
4. Put onto a greased baking tray. Brush with beaten egg and bake on the top shelf for 7-8 minutes until the scones are golden brown.
5. Remove the scones and place on a wire rack to cool.

Use the Nutrition Program

- Enter the ingredients into the program in My Recipes.
- What is the nutrition for 100g of the main 8 nutrients?
- Complete the chart below.

Scones		
	100g	portion
Energy kcal		
Protein		
Carbohydrate		
Fat		
Saturated fat		
Fibre		
Salt		

Make a healthier scones recipe

Change the recipe and see how the nutrition for 100g changes.
Try to increase the fibre and reduce the fat in this recipe.
Write out the new recipe and complete the nutrition chart or export the chart from the program.

Make one savoury recipe and one sweet recipe.
Savoury ideas
cheese, Marmite, herbs, onions, leeks

Sweet ideas
sultanas, currants, sugar, spices, cherries, banana

Scones - healthy recipe - savoury		
	100g	portion
Energy kcal		
Protein		
Carbohydrate		
Fat		
Saturated fat		
Fibre		
Salt		

Scones - healthy recipe - sweet		
	100g	portion
Energy kcal		
Protein		
Carbohydrate		
Fat		
Saturated fat		
Fibre		
Salt		

My scone recipe savoury   My scone recipe sweet

What changes did you make to the recipe to increase the fibre?

What changes did you make to the recipe to lower the fat?

Veggie burger and Beef burger - compare the nutrition

My Recipes
Compare the nutrition of a veggie burger and a beef burger.

Veggie burger
Serves 4

Ingredients
1 carrot, diced
1 onion, sliced
1 celery stick, finely sliced
1 garlic clove, finely chopped
1 small leek, finely sliced
6 tbsp oil
1 x 400g canned kidney beans, washed and drained
200g brown rice, boiled
2 tbs parsley, chopped
Salt and pepper

Method
1. Cook the rice in boiling water.
2. Fry the carrot, onion, celery, garlic and leek in 3 tbs oil until soft.
3. Add kidney beans and cooked rice and stir into the vegetables. Mash everything and add salt and pepper.
4. Cool and shape into patties 8 cm across and 2 cm deep.
5. Heat the rest of the oil and fry the veggie burgers for 3-4 minutes each side until golden brown and crisp.
6. Serve with a bun or baked potato.

Beef burger
Serves 4

Ingredients
900g minced beef
1 pinch salt
fresh ground black pepper
2 tbsp vegetable oil

Method
1. Mix together the beef, salt and pepper.
2. Shape into 4 burgers.
3. Heat the oil and fry the burgers for 4-6 minutes each side.
4. Serve with a bun or baked potato.

Use The Nutrition Program
- Enter the ingredients for the veggie burgers and beef burgers – they both serve 4.
- Fill in the charts to show the amount of nutrients in 100g and a portion for each burger.

Veggie burger and Beefburger - compare the nutrition

Veggie burger	100g	portion
Energy kcal		
Protein		
Carbohydrate		
Fat		
Saturated fat		
Fibre		
Salt		

Beef burger	100g	portion
Energy kcal		
Protein		
Carbohydrate		
Fat		
Saturated fat		
Fibre		
Salt		

To do

1. Which burger has
The highest kcal? ....
The most protein? ....
The most carbohydrate? ....
The most fat? ....
The highest saturated fat? ....
The most fibre? ....
The most salt? ....

2. Make another recipe and enter the results in the Nutrition Program. Is this recipe healthier?

4. Which burger would you recommend to a friend and why?

Extension work
Add a burger bun to each portion. How does that change the nutrition?
Remove the bun and add a baked potato. How does that change the nutrition?
Which is the best choice - a bun or a baked potato? Give your reasons.

Spaghetti with bacon and cream - lower the fat

My Recipes
This traditional Italian recipe for spaghetti, bacon and cream was created before we were concerned about eating less fat, so it is not a healthy choice!
The aim of this task is to look at the nutrition for this recipe and see how you can change the ingredients to lower the fat.

Spaghetti with bacon and cream
Serves 4

Ingredients
15 ml vegetable oil
3 cloves garlic, crushed
25g butter
175g bacon cut into strips
350g dried spaghetti
Water to cook
75g grated Parmesan cheese
150 ml single cream
1 tsp salt and black pepper

Method
1. Bring a large saucepan of water to the boil and cook the spaghetti according to packet instructions until it is chewy and soft. Drain to remove the water and put in a bowl. Spaghetti absorbs 2 ½ times its weight in water.
2. Heat the oil and fry the garlic for 2-3 minutes.
3. Add the butter and bacon and cook until the bacon becomes crisp.
4. Mix the Parmesan, cream, salt and pepper in a bowl then stir into the cooked spaghetti and add the bacon with its fat.
5. Serve immediately.

Use The Nutrition Program
- Enter the ingredients for the spaghetti dish.
- Fill in the chart to show the amount of nutrients in 100g and a portion.
- Now make a healthier version by changing the ingredients.

Spaghetti with bacon and cream		
	100g	portion
Energy kcal		
Protein		
Carbohydrate		
Fat		
Saturated fat		
Fibre		
Salt		

Spaghetti with bacon and cream - lower the fat

To do
Create a new lower fat, healthier recipe
and test it out.

Spaghetti recipe - healthier version		
	100g	portion
Energy kcal		
Protein		
Carbohydrate		
Fat		
Saturated fat		
Fibre		
Salt		

1. List the ingredients that you would change in the spaghetti with bacon and cream to make the dish lower in fat.

....

....

....

2. What is the fat content of the traditional recipe and your lower fat recipe (100g)?

Traditional ....

Lower fat ....

3. What is the difference in the energy value in 100g of each dish?

Traditional..

Lower fat..

4. What other foods can you serve with these dishes to make a nutritious meal? Give your reasons.
Test out your ideas using the Nutrition Program.

Extension work
This dish is high in salt. How can the sodium (salt) be reduced?

Macaroni cheese - Make a recipe healthier

My Recipes
In this task you will put in the ingredients for Macaroni cheese into The Nutrition Program and see its nutritional value. You can then make a healthier version to lower the fat and compare the two recipes.

Macaroni cheese
Serves 2

Ingredients
150g dried macaroni
375 ml water for cooking
300 ml milk
25g butter
25g flour
100g grated cheese
Salt and pepper
1 teaspoon Worcestershire sauce
25g grated cheese for garnish
Tomato cut into slices

Method
1. Cook the macaroni in a large pan of boiling water for 10 – 12 minutes, stirring occasionally.
2. Strain the macaroni through a colander to remove the water and put back into the saucepan.
3. Make the sauce. Put the milk, butter and flour into a small saucepan and whisk over the heat until the sauce thickens.
4. Remove from the heat and add the grated cheese then season with salt, pepper, Worcestershire sauce.
5. Stir the sauce into the macaroni and spoon into a serving dish.
6. Sprinkle on the extra grated cheese and decorate with the slices of tomato.
7. Reheat in a hot oven for 15 – 20 minutes until the top is golden.

Note – when you cook any pasta, you need to add an two and a half times the weight of water to the recipe for analysis. This is because pasta absorbs water when it is cooked.

Macaroni cheese - Make a recipe healthier

Use the Nutrition Program
Enter the ingredients into The Nutrition Program.
Fill in the chart which shows the nutrition for 100g and a portion.

To do
This Macaroni cheese recipe is high in saturated fat, so you can try and lower the fat content by
- Changing the type of milk or cheese used
- Adding some vegetables such as leeks, peas or courgettes.
- Choosing a different fat to make the sauce with.

How do you do this?
Go to My recipes and click on Macaroni Cheese.
At the bottom of the screen is Make a healthier version.
Click this and see the first recipe, which you can alter.
Look at the amount of fat in butter. Find an alternative which is healthier.
Replace the whole milk with semi skimmed milk.
Add some peas and other vegetables to the dish.
Fill in the chart which shows the nutrition for 100g and a portion for your healthier dish and compare results.

Macaroni cheese		
	100g	portion
Energy kcal		
Protein		
Carbohydrate		
Fat		
Saturated fat		
Fibre		
Salt		
cost		

Macaroni cheese - healthier version		
	100g	portion
Energy kcal		
Protein		
Carbohydrate		
Fat		
Saturated fat		
Fibre		
Salt		
cost		

Pizza - lower the salt

My Recipes
The easiest way to lower the salt is to
add less salt and salty foods to a recipe.
This is a recipe for a very salty pizza!

Pizza recipe
Serves 4

Ingredients
250g strong flour
2 tablespoons olive oil
1 level teaspoon salt
100 ml lukewarm water
2 teaspoons dried yeast
½ teaspoon sugar

Topping
200g canned, chopped tomatoes
100g grated cheese
6 slices salami
12 olives
2 slices ham

Method
1. Set the oven at 220ºC, Gas 7.
2. Put the flour, oil, salt, yeast and sugar in a bowl and stir in the warm water. Mix to a dough and turn out onto a floured board.
3. Knead the dough until smooth and elastic.
4. Grease a large baking tray and pat the dough onto the tray until it covers the base. Leave to increase in size.
5. Spoon on the chopped tomatoes and cover with grated cheese, salami, olives and strips of ham.
6. Bake for 20 minutes until well risen and golden.

Use The Nutrition Program
• Enter the ingredients for the pizza.
• Fill in the chart to show the amount of nutrients in 100g and a portion.

Pizza		
	100g	portion
Energy kcal		
Protein		
Carbohydrate		
Fat		
Saturated fat		
Fibre		
Salt		

Pizza - lower the salt

To do
Change the pizza recipe to lower the salt content.
Think about
- replacing the salty food with ingredients with less salt
- increasing the amount of vegetables.

Test out the recipe to see how it looks and tastes.
Compare the salt content of each recipe to show the difference.

Lowering the salt in the pizza
In the recipe section, choose
Make a Healthier version and change the ingredients to lower the salt.
Look at the foods that are high in salt
- Ham
- Salami
- Olives
- Salt

We should eat no more than 6g of salt a day

Remove these foods and replace them with foods with less salt but which are full of flavour - red peppers, courgette. Remove the salt from the pizza dough and reduce the amount of cheese.

My pizza recipe

Pizza - less salty		
	100g	portion
Energy kcal		
Protein		
Carbohydrate		
Fat		
Saturated fat		
Fibre		
Salt		

High energy oat bar - make a food label

My Recipes
This recipe is a basic recipe for a high energy bar made from oats.
Your task is to adapt the recipe by adding seeds and fruit to add crunchiness and colour to the recipe. This will also change the nutritional value and the cost. Find out how you have changed the nutritional value of your new recipe and test it out.

High energy oat bar
Makes 16 squares

Ingredients for basic recipe
2 tablespoons golden syrup (60g)
80g brown sugar
100g margarine or butter
200g rolled oats

Method
1. Put the oven on at 175°C/ Gas 5.
2. Heat the tablespoon over the gas or in hot water then measure the tablespoons of golden syrup.
3. In a saucepan melt the sugar, margarine and golden syrup.
4. Stir in the oats and spoon into a 22 cm square tin and smooth down.
5. Bake for 25 minutes – a bit longer if you want it crunchy.
6. Take out of the oven and mark into 16 squares. Leave to cool.

Use the Nutrition Program
• Put the recipe into the Nutrition Program and save the work.
• Produce a label for the High energy bar.
• Go to the Food Label section and complete the sections:
　　Storage info
　　Manufactured by
　　Use by
• In Appearance you can add a food picture of your product and change the label style.
• Export your label and either print it off or save it into your work.

The label for the high energy bar shows that the bar is high in sugar, fat and saturated fat.

To do
Adapt the recipe and add other ingredients to replace some of the oats.

High energy oat bar - make a food label

These are ingredients you can add to the basic recipe to add flavour and colour:
- 50g mixed seeds
- 30g mixed peel
- 20g glace cherries, chopped.

Extra ingredients that add other nutrients:
Mashed banana, sultanas, raisins, dried cranberries, dried blueberries, chocolate, carob.

Test it out
Put the basic recipes into the Nutrition Program.

Save the recipe and view the nutrition analysis.
Now adapt the recipe by adding some seeds, nuts, fruit, dried fruit or chocolate.
Compare this recipe with the basic recipe.
How has the cost changed?
How has the nutrition changed?
Make a food label of the new product.
What allergens are found in the new recipe?

What would be your selling price for this product and how would you describe the new product?

High energy bar		
	100g	portion
Energy kcal		
Protein		
Carbohydrate		
Fat		
Saturated fat		
Fibre		
Salt		
cost		

High energy bar with seeds and other ingredients		
	100g	portion
Energy kcal		
Protein		
Carbohydrate		
Fat		
Saturated fat		
Fibre		
Salt		
cost		

Couscous salad – looking at allergens

My Recipes
In this worksheet, you will put the recipe into The Nutrition Program to look at the allergens it might contain.
These are the allergens that are listed on food labels.
Some people have to be careful of foods which can make them unwell.

Allergens
- Wheat
- Gluten
- Eggs
- Fish
- Peanuts
- Soya
- Milk
- Nuts
- Mustard
- Sesame seeds
- Shellfish

wheat is an allergen

Couscous salad
Serves 4

Ingredients
200g cooked couscous
½ green pepper, seeded and finely chopped (50g)
1 red skinned eating apple, cored and chopped (50g)
1 ½ tbs peanuts (50g)
1 tbs raisins (25g)
salt and freshly ground pepper
1 tbs olive oil,
2 tsp lemon juice or cider vinegar

Method
Place all the ingredients in a large bowl and toss well together.

Use the Nutrition Program
Looking at allergens
Put the recipe into the Nutrition Program.
Look at Nutrition Info and at the bottom of the screen you will see allergens.

Couscous salad – looking at allergens

To do
Change the Couscous salad recipe to remove the allergens. Your aim is to have an allergen free recipe.

To replace the wheat and gluten allergens replace the ingredient which is made from wheat. In this case it will be couscous. Replace the peanuts too.
Try out some other ingredients to make a different salad and see what allergens are listed instead.
Write out your new recipe and make it to see how tasty it is.

> My salad recipe

For couscous salad it shows wheat and gluten, and peanuts as the allergens.

Extension work
Find the recipes for the following dishes and put them into The Nutrition Program.
Complete the chart below to show the allergens, if any.
- Cheese and tomato pizza
- Fish cakes
- Chicken korma
- Dhal
- Fresh fruit salad
- Milk smoothie
You can find recipes on the internet.

Recipe	Allergens
Cheese and tomato pizza	
Fish cakes	
Chicken korma	
Dhal	
Fresh fruit salad	
Milk smoothie	

Carrot cake – costing and nutrition

My Recipes
The aim of this task is to find the cost for a portion and the whole cake. This is useful if you are making the cake for fund raising or making a cake with a limited budget. If you are fund raising you can decide the selling price for a portion and the whole cake so that you make a profit.
You can also find the nutritional value of the cake and the allergens. Remember, this is a cake and is eaten as a treat!

Carrot cake
Serves 8

Ingredients
350g carrots, peeled & grated
150ml vegetable oil
200g caster sugar
3 medium eggs
200g plain flour
2 level teaspoons baking powder
½ level teaspoon mixed spice
juice of 1 orange

Topping
200g Quark
40g icing sugar
zest of 1 orange

Method
1.   Heat the oven to 125°C, Gas Mark 3. Grease and line a 1kg loaf tin or 20cm cake tin.
2.   In a bowl mix together the oil, sugar and eggs.
3.   Sieve in the flour, baking powder and mixed spice.
4.   Stir in the grated carrots and juice of an orange.
5.   Spoon into the tin and bake for 45 minutes or until the cake is firm. Cool the cake on a wire rack.
6.   For the topping, mix the Quark with icing sugar and orange zest and spread over the top of the cake.
7.   Take a digital picture of the cake if you want to create a food label.

Use the Nutrition Program
• Enter the ingredients into The Nutrition Program.
• Using the Cost Analysis section, find out the cost for a portion and the whole cake.
• Fill in the chart. What is your selling price?
• Now work on the food label and add the picture of your cake or use an image from the internet.
• What is the nutrition for a portion of carrot cake? You can see from the Traffic lights that the cake is high in sugar but this is normal for a cake!
• Print out the results or copy and paste into other work.

Carrot cake – costing and nutrition

To do
What is the nutrition for a portion of
carrot cake?
Fill in the chart to show the nutrition.

Carrot cake cost			
total weight	cost 100g	cost recipe	cost portion

Changing a cake recipe can be quite
difficult as you may not get a good result
if you alter the ingredients too much.

Complete this label to show the
information you need on the Carrot cake
if it is for sale.

Carrot cake nutrition		
	100g	portion
Energy kcal		
Protein		
Carbohydrate		
Fat		
Saturated fat		
Fibre		
Salt		

Carrot cake label	
Cost for portion	
Calories in a portion	
Fat	
Fibre	
Allergens	

Extension work
Find some recipes for other cakes and
test them in the program. For example,
Victoria Sandwich, Gingerbread, Eccles
cakes, Bakewell tart. Compare these
results with the nutrition for the carrot
cake.

Your diet

Analyse your diet and see how good it is.
Try and improve it and see the changes.

Complete the chart to show what foods
you have eaten in one day.

My day's diet	
Breakfast	amount
Lunch	
Afternoon food	
Supper	
Snacks and drinks	

Your diet

Use the Nutrition Program
- Click My Diets
- Create a new diet
- Enter the diet name
- Start day
- Age
- Sex – you choose male or female.

Enter the foods that you have eaten. The program helps with the weights.

Analyse your diet
- Click Diet Chart at the bottom of the screen.
- See if your diet provides for your nutrition needs.
- Click Diet Analysis Chart. This shows you other nutrients in your diet.
- You can export this chart and save it onto Word, Powerpoint or Publisher.

To do
Make a healthier version of your diet.
Click Make a healthier version.
Change some of the foods.
Look at the charts and see if it has improved.
Answer the questions to show how your diet has improved.

Questions

How healthy is your diet?
Write a little about it and the results.

What changes did you make to have a healthier diet?

How have the charts changed to show your results?

Glossary

Alcohol
Alcohol is high in calories and so can make you put on weight. It's also a diuretic, which means it makes the body lose more water than usual.

Allergens
The range of ingredients in food products that cause common food allergies include wheat, milk, eggs, sesame, soya, nuts, fish, gluten.

AOAC
Association of Official Analytical Chemists (AOAC) method for fibre analysis - this method includes lignin and resistant starch. The GDA is 24g a day for men and women.

Biotin
Biotin helps the body turn the food we eat into energy.

Calcium
Calcium helps build strong bones and teeth. RNI 700 mg for men and 700 mg for women a day.

Calorie
Calorie is a unit of measurement for energy.

Carbohydrates
Carbohydrates are a source of energy. Recommended intake is not less than 50% food energy.

Carotene
Carotene is turned into vitamin A in the body. Beta-carotene gives yellow and orange fruit and vegetables their colour.

Chloride
Chloride helps the body digest the food we eat because it's an essential component of the juices in the stomach and intestines.

Cholesterol
Dietary cholesterol is the type that we get from our food - it has much less effect on the level of cholesterol in our blood than the amount of saturated fat we eat.

Copper
Copper helps produce red and white blood cells and triggers the release of iron to form haemoglobin.

Costs
The costs are based on supermarket prices - these change and you can put in your own prices.

DRV
Dietary Reference Value - benchmark intakes of energy and nutrients.

Fat
Fat helps the body absorb some vitamins, it's a good source of energy and a source of the essential fatty acids that the body can't make itself. The DRV for fat is not more than 35% food energy.

Fibre
Fibre is needed to keep the gut healthy and prevent constipation. Fibre is measured as NSP or AOAC.

Folate
Folate is needed for the normal structure of the neural tube in developing embryos. RNI 200 ug for men and women a day.

Fructose
Fructose is a simple sugar that is found in honey, tree fruits and some root vegetables.

Fruit and vegetables
People who eat diets rich in fruits and vegetables have a lower incidence of heart disease, diabetes, dementia, stroke and certain types of cancer.

GDA
Guideline Daily Amounts used on food labels. For example Women – 2000 Calories, 90g Sugars, 70g Fat, 20g Saturates, 6g Salt

Glucose
Glucose is a simple sugar and source of energy.

Iodine
Iodine helps make the thyroid hormones which keep cells and the metabolic rate healthy. RNI 140 ug for men and women a day.

Iron
Iron helps make red blood cells, which carry oxygen around the body. RNI 8.7mg for men and 14.8 mg for women a day.

kcal
kilocalorie - a measurement of energy in food.

Glossary

kJ
kilojoule - a measurement of energy in food.

Lactose
Lactose is a disaccharide and is found in milk and milk products.

Magnesium
Magnesium helps the body use energy. Needed for healthy tissues and bones. RNI 300 mg for men and 270 mg for women a day.

Maltose
Maltose is a disaccharide formed from two units of glucose.

Manganese
Manganese helps make and activate some of the enzymes in the body.

Mono-unsaturates
Unsaturated fats can be a healthy choice. These types of fats can reduce cholesterol levels and provide us with the essential fatty acids that the body needs.

Net weight
The net weight on the packaging is the weight or volume of the product without the weight of the packaging.

Niacin
Niacin is needed for the release of energy from carbohydrates and protein.RNI 6.6 mg for men and for women a day.

NSP
Term for indigestible carbohydrates which are found in foods of plant origin. Englyst fibre (non-starch polysaccharides) includes both insoluble fibre (cellulose, insoluble non-cellulosic polysaccharides) and soluble fibre (soluble cellulosic polysaccharides). Recommended intake 18g a day for adults.

Pantothenate
A water-soluble vitamin involved in the Kreb's energy production cycle

Phosphorus
Phosphorus helps build strong bones and teeth and helps release energy from food. RNI 550 mg for men and for women a day.

Polyunsaturated fats
Unsaturated fats can be a healthy choice. These types of fats can reduce cholesterol levels and provide us with the essential fatty acids that the body needs.

Portion
The amount by weight of a food product that people like to eat - for example, the weight of a slice of pizza.

Potassium
Potassium controls the balance of fluids in the body and may also help lower blood pressure. RNI 3500 mg for men and for women a day.

Protein
Protein is needed for growth and repair, and also a source of energy.

QUID
Quantitative Ingredient Declaration - ingredients on a food label are sorted into order of weight with the heaviest first.

Retinol
A form of Vitamin A which is needed for growth, development and eyesight. RNI 700 ug for men and 600 ug for women a day.

Riboflavin
Riboflavin is needed for the release of energy from carbohydrates and protein. RNI 1.3 mg for men and 1.1mg for women a day.

RNI
Reference Nutrient Intake (RNI) is the amount of a specific nutrient which is sufficient for almost all individuals.

Salt
Salt is made of sodium chloride. GDA for salt is 6g a day for adults and 4g a day for children.

Saturates/ Saturated fat
Too much saturated fat can increase the amount of cholesterol in the blood, which increases the chance of developing heart disease. The DRV is not more than 11% food energy.

Selenium
Selenium plays an important role in our immune system's function, in thyroid hormone metabolism and in reproduction. RNI 75 ug for men and 60 ug for women a day.

Glossary

Sodium
Sodium helps to keep the level of fluids in the body balanced. But we must not eat too much. RNI 1600 mg for men and for women a day. Sodium and chloride make salt. To change sodium into salt, divide the sodium (mg) by 1000 and multiply by 2.5.

Starch
Starch is a good source of energy.

Storage instructions
This is the information on how to keep the product. Chilled food should be kept in the refrigerator, ambient food such as flour and canned food is stored at room temperature in a cool, dry place.

Sucrose
Sucrose is table sugar. Too much sugar in the diet is linked to tooth decay. GDA is 90g a day for women, 120g for men.

Sugar
Sugar adds flavour and sweetness to foods and is a source of energy. Frequent consumption of sugary foods is associated with an increased tendency to tooth decay. The GDA for sugar is 90g per day for women and children and 120g a day for men.

Thiamin
Thiamin is needed for the release of energy from carbohydrates and protein. RNI 1mg for men and 0.8mg for women a day.

Traffic light system
This shows the colours green, amber and red for food products for 100g. Used on food labels to show which foods we should eat more or less of.

Trans Fats/ Trans fatty acids
Trans fats have a similar effect on blood cholesterol as saturated fats - they raise the type of cholesterol in the blood that increases the risk of heart disease.

Tryptophan
An essential amino acid that your body does not have the ability to synthesise.

Vitamin A
Vitamin A is needed for growth, development and eyesight. It is calculated from retinol and carotene figures. RNI 700 ug for men and 600 ug for women a day.

Vitamin B12
Vitamin B12 is needed for blood cells and nerve function. RNI 1.5 ug for men and for women a day.

Vitamin B6
Vitamin B6 is essential for good health and red blood cell metabolism. RNI 1.4mg for men and 1.2mg for women a day.

Vitamin C
Vitamin C is needed for healthy skin and tissue, and to aid the absorption of iron. RNI 40 mg a day for men and women.

Vitamin D
Vitamin D helps regulate the amount of calcium and phosphate in the body.

Vitamin E
Vitamin E helps protect cell membranes by acting as an antioxidant.

Vitamin K1
Vitamin K helps wounds heal properly because it's needed for blood clotting.

Water
Chemical reactions that happen in our cells need water. We also need water for our blood to be able to carry nutrients around the body.

Zinc
Zinc is required for tissue growth and repair. RNI 9.5mg for men and 7mg for women a day.

Nutrition Crossword 1- use Glossary for this work

www.CrosswordWeaver.com

ACROSS

1 Type of diet that provides a range of nutrients.
4 Table sugar.
9 Guideline Daily Amount.
11 Mineral which helps thyroid hormones.
12 Method of fibre analysis.
14 Needed for growth and repair.
17 Form of vitamin A.
18 The Englyst method of analysing fibre.
19 Indigestible part of food.
20 Quantitative Ingredient Declaration.
22 Simple sugar.
23 Dietary Reference Values.
24 Type of fat which can reduce cholesterol.

DOWN

2 Measured in calories and joules.
3 Vitamin needed for release of energy.
5 Mineral which builds bones and teeth.
6 Milk sugar.
7 Fruit sugar.
8 The foods and drink eaten during the day.
10 Needed for neural tube of embryos.
13 Unit of measurement of energy.
14 Mineral which helps build strong bones and teeth.
15 Helps make red blood cells.
16 Range of ingredients in food that cause reactions if eaten.
17 Reference Nutrient Intake.
21 Sodium chloride.

My meals crossword

ACROSS

- **1** Flour with high fibre.
- **7** Name for salt in food.
- **8** Source of protein.
- **10** Meat alternative.
- **14** Source of salt.
- **15** Type of carbohydrate.
- **17** Source of carbohydrate.
- **18** Needed for growth and tissue repair.
- **19** Needed for red blood cells.
- **20** Type of carbohydrate.
- **22** Type of fat.
- **24** Fortified with calcium.
- **27** Iron deficiency.
- **28** Vitamin C.

DOWN

- **2** Source of folate.
- **3** Needed for growth and repair.
- **4** Type of fruit high in vitamin C.
- **5** Name for table sugars and jam.
- **6** Source of calcium.
- **9** Type of fat.
- **11** Essential for a healthy digestive system.
- **12** What happens to teeth with too much sugar.
- **13** Needed for strong bones.
- **16** Essential for blood cells.
- **17** Source of fat.
- **20** Beans with calcium.
- **21** Fruit with high vitamin A.
- **23** Source of zinc.
- **25** Provides twice the calories of carbohydrate.
- **26** Source of carbohydrate.

Nutrition Crossword answers

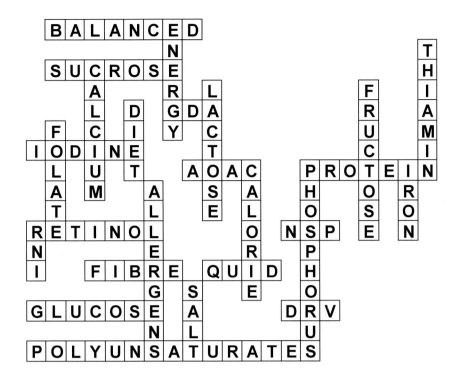

My meals crossword

Solution:

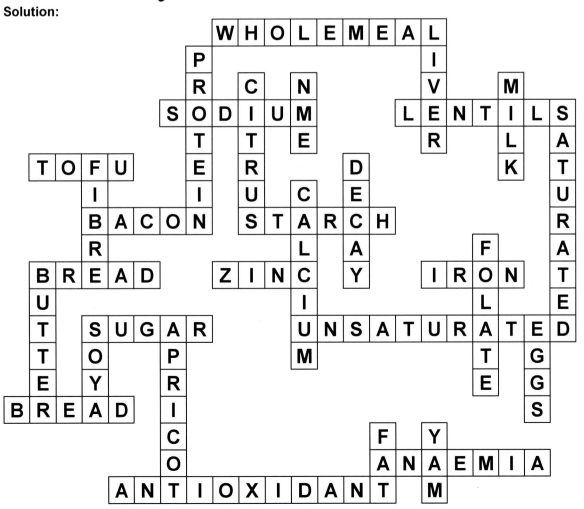

School account set up guide

Teacher log in
Login at
www.nutritionprogram.co.uk/login
using your Teacher login details.

Student username and passwords
Login to update your students account details.
In My Account you will see the teacher's account and then the list of usernames and passwords.
Each student can be given their own named account or you can use those on the automatic system. When you want to change the users, Clear the account, which empties it, then type in the new name. Finally Update the account and the student has a fresh account.

Student log in
Students log into the program directly using their allocated username and passwords. They can login by using the link below www.nutritonprogram.co.uk/login and choosing the Student Login.

Their account is for their personal use and can be accessed anywhere where there is internet access.

Removing student accounts
When students have left the school, you can remove their accounts and change the username. Clear the account of work.
Give the new student the account with their own username.

Do not give students your teacher login otherwise they will all use your account and the program will not work.

Submit food
If you cannot find a food on the database, then in Recipes, you can see Submit new ingredient at the bottom of the screen. We will try to find the nutrition for the ingredient then add it to the database.

Food costs
We try and update the cost of ingredients every 6 months, but are always happy to get an email from you if you think the prices are incorrect.

The Program is online so requires no installation. You get a username and password which you can use anywhere as long as you have a computer and an internet connection.

The Nutrition Program uses Flash and will work on a PC and a MAC. It does rely on your internet connection to work so if your network is slow you may experience issues.

If the program is working slowly, check with your IT support team at school and ask
1) is a firewall blocking access,
2) what is the speed of the internet service provider - is it fast enough for this program,
3) is the school network set up properly,
4) does your system go through a proxy that filters internet content and caches,
5) are you using laptops on shared wireless access points which will slow access down?
Tip - avoid getting all your students logging in at the same time. Load the program in batches of 5 students.

Why are there no prices for organic and fair trade ingredients?
A. The Food Standards Agency report says that there is no nutritional difference between organic and ordinary food, so we have not included them in the listing. I know that the prices are different but you will need to Edit and add your own for the moment.

If you need more help, please email us at support@nutritionprogram.co.uk

The Nutrition Program is owned by Ridgwell Press and designed and produced by Jenny Ridgwell and Simon Ridgwell.